PENINSU

PEN INS ULA

PENINSULA

First published by Egg Box Publishing in association
with Durham University Part of UEA Publishing Project Ltd
International
A CIO record of this book is available from the British Library

Peninsula is typeset in Calisto MT
Design and typesetting by Ronja Rønning
Printed and bound in the UK by Imprint Digital
Distributed by NBN International

ISBN: 978-1-911343-90-5

THE PENINSULA TEAM

CONTENT

POETRY

Josh Allsop

11 Snag

12 Spiral afterimage

13 Bathysphere

Lucy Atkinson

14 Rose-Tinted

15 Moonlight

16 The Songs We Sing When We Think Of You

17 We That Wander

Rory Clarkson

18 Ghost

19 The March of Spring Brings the Cruelest Shoots

Laura Day

20-21 Magnolia Walls

22-23 An important anniversary

24-25 Getaway Car

Cassidy Harvard-Davies

26-27 monkey bars

28-29 four foot

30 winter on the isle of wight

Finn Haunch

31 Down Fulneck Beck

Avleen Kaur

32 Open Again

33 Daarji's Photo Album

34 Karan

35 Guns and Flutes

Annabel Mahoney

36 Symbolist Letter from Madrigal to Galahad

37 Galahad replies;

38 Green Willow

Victoria Penn

39 The Changeling

Chutian Xiao

40 Empty Town

41 The Master

PROSE

Janina Arndt

43-47 Album of Written Photographs

Theo Breet

48-53 Wither; Ruminate

Rosie Crocker

54-56 Bute

Ethan C. Hemmati
57-61 Blue Moon

Matthew McKenzie
62-67 Rainbow states

Kleopatra Olympiou
68-73 Unbelonging

Upasana Pradhan
74-78 Dear Zoya,

Imogen Sharpe
79-83 An Old Song Playing in Another Room

James Shiers
84-89 Do Not Refreeze

Claudia Sterbini
90-91 The Sound of her Essence

92-96 *Rachael Wanogho*
Hustle Tomorrow, Not Today

97-98 *Tula Wild*
Brake Lights

99-103 *Wu, You (Helen)*
An Accident at the Underground Railway Station

POETRY

Snag

Hidden in the crucible they sat shoulder to shoulder
catching each other's breath,
this tandem moment of bony limbs
under taffeta. Jank, the lot of it,
peeling close to the edge of words
that I might have taken intravenous like
so much mercury
filing slim and lithe down the wiring; transmutation
caused in essence by the breakdown, restructured capillary
wall in finer cladding, something shown off
at a flower show, averting eyes from Kensington.

Univocal icon, our construct/affront/
prideful impaled, spoken clay posture crumbling into babbling
before dry, that got funding permissions and a good
college try put to it, and what we have is tongues
wagging/uttering nothing of the sort
that finds anybody a room in the rubble.
Some kind of wax or polythene, might as well have been
feathers
for the weight of their…sorry,
all smoke on the mirrors.

Spiral afterimage

He fumbles with the rifle, comic mittens shed,
lambent fingers catch the clinker
of last sun – haloed fire on pared cuticles.
In the calving body rupture is gradual,
spreading, starts at an inception point I won't think about.
We skim sulphurs in palms,
relish the lithic whip
as they glance off the sheet
casting out submarine echoes –
the only sound rushes away from me.
Foot pivot, screw out mud in shavings
like an ice core on the end of your leg,
leaving the ground surge hot, steam
obscuring the stars in glasses.
The only sound left:
the dead belt twisting.

Want to ignite a star?
Passing into dusk hold the heft of it close,
loose scraps filing between your fingers.
Bundled orb, crack it. Bathe the land amnion
blooming into filter of Petworth fug
(sans stag; leave us, xanthopsic fury)
at the edge where the light catches itself on mud crags,
we caught ash in our mouths, but the sound
of the click-break snaps just so, drowns us,
leaves the glow trapped at a Zeno point
somewhere aloft, hung.

Bathysphere

Scum on the lip
we kneel
dip knuckles
into foaming jade.
So we believe that, do we?
These bubbles
link to a deep
beyond the confines
of architectonics,
the housing of trunks
and podes of innumerable graces.

Instead of the slope
we have the precipice. Handling
the back of your neck
I press you
through the altered glass,
painting my forearms,
your entire head,
with a film and
pronate a view
to the underneath
of where we situate ourselves.

Hands raised,
there are clefts in the palm
that catch algae in arterial clags,
I'm asking what you saw
and you're just coughing.

Rose-Tinted

Amour brisé

I nurse a glass filled with the memory of you.
Honey. Buttercups on my lips.
It's not about loss or numbness or pain.
Everything is rose-tinted after midnight. After.
I've been hunting it. That something,
unreachable on the tip of my brain.
A kind of melancholy. There's nothing else
to do. But you were like a springtime;
like an open flame. What endures
such heat?
The tallest pine tree can't
endure the smallest quake
and I am not enough. Not you.
The world moves slightly slower. No
forgiveness. Only memory. Troubled water.
Love is just the prologue to the story.
How does it end? How? Do we end?

Moonlight

There's something about moonlight. Not like
they told me in stories about old Gaelic wisps
movies about people who fall instantly in love
and out of debt.
It sits deeper. Constancy.
Something colder. Further away.
Maybe it makes me feel like home.
Maybe it makes me feel-

The Songs We Sing When We Think Of You

It's almost nostalgic. All of us together.
Like Mam in her punk phase.
Liquorice. Honey in my tea.
Something new. Feeling old.
Like how we've all grown so
different. Grown so sad.
They hang yellow ribbons to remember
your life. On the tree we used to climb.
Someone talks to me about lamenting. About grief.
But there's only laughter in my memory.
Blurry moments burning neon.
I am trying to remember this;
You. I don't want to forget.

We That Wander

They say now he's in the quiet place.
A place we never dared to go.
A stranger. Yet he shares our name.
    I wonder, can he still hear the wisdom
    In the sound of the rain?
Or feel the footsteps on the wet grass?
Stone and cold.
    But does he remember
    all the things our father said?
"Remember son. My son remember,"
    Spitting black with ashy lungs,
"My son,
    only we that wander
Truly know the way back home."

Ghost

We now share a past; watching the raven
strafe over the river in search of safe haven.

What hands have those hands touched — I should not know?
They're from a foreign time you're yet to show.

Support – an idea shadowing words we feared.
Seconds slipping as the lie of ice cleared.

Opaque looks were all we shared, they had to be,
freeing up our divided mystery;

streetlights easier than the gaze of day.
We split smiles, accepting the moment: stay?

To drink is to care. We consumed our time;
memories which now exist inside.

I'm sure that one day mist will block the view,
silencing the three piercing towers of you.

The March of Spring Brings the Cruelest Shoots

It was once the realm of cliché
kissing in the eastward lie
as we believed the simple path of day.
It was lost in a clear night's sky

when warmth was what we needed.
Distance held us out of reach,
skin searching for any skin
until there was only an overlooked breach.

The sun will rise again,
predictable, but not always the same.
As its rays tire clouds will keep
their hearts alive. We'll bond as we sleep.

Your laugh lives on, echoing within me.
Sometimes my fingers still curl without yours.
Life is not conditional on any one
moment; do we want it to be?

Waking just to open the same doors:
we only live if we accept what's done.

Magnolia Walls

She sits, swallowing
words.
'Goodbye' splutters.
It lands in a cough.
'Why' chokes; like a kind of
vandalism.
Spray-painted in black on the back of the
throat.
It makes no sense.

Halcyon days fall
quiet
In the
magnolia-stained
Walls-of-the-ward.
'Love makes you realise that other people are real',
she says,
On empty breath.

'Lips are temporary
But kisses are
permanent.
The hallmarks of love
passed'.
She stops.
Gifting a minute's silence;
And settles into the room.

He's not the first, he won't be the
last.
Life splinters against the magnolia
skies
Of ward forty nine – sixth floor –
room five.
He's one of history's boys
now,
And she's a lover with clipped
breath.
As one life empties, one welcomes
Death.

An important anniversary

Who knew that Saturday could be so
harsh?
I suppose it's on this day, one year from the
last,
That I find out just
what
I am made of.

Am I composed of
stone,
And solipsistic
strength
Like some virago?

Or am I trapped in the human
position
With dulcet voice
Looking for a bridge
to burn?

I fear it's the latter.

As I wake on this
Saturday
And discover that my good
mood
Should antedate the dawn, I
sigh.

Breakfast tastes like
defeat.

My bed becomes the
defences
Of some wartime fort.

From the darkness,
Weapons are drawn,
And battle commences.

I wave a white flag in
vain.
Suddenly the bucolic
setting
I'd made assume the furniture of
home[1]
Is dead.

In the distance there's
Sunday
Waving innocent
promises.
But Saturday wants
blood.

I'm afraid to move.
It hurts to breathe.
My heart can't beat.
Please, Sunday.

Hold me.

[1] W. H. Auden, September 1, 1939, l. 51

Getaway Car

Today I remembered what it was like to be
held.
It happened before, but I had almost
Forgotten.
I remembered that it was warm,
tight;
It was like I had stolen the sun and
you –
You were the getaway
car.

As part of some foiled escape, we took the sun
with us.
We risked the open road, longing for new
skies.
And when we found the skies, we planted
the sun.
And it was ours;
Ours for the keeping, our tool
for
Counting the days.

I remember that we counted,
slowly.
And when people told us that it was impossible to steal
the sun,
We knew otherwise.
We had stolen it, in a feat of
mischief,
And had left the world standing on the
platform,
Waiting for the sun to appear
again.

But then I remembered that the sun went
out.
And we paused, on the
road,
Stopped traffic.
I just wanted to be sure of
you,
But even you were
erased,
Gone with the sun.

But I remembered that, even though the sun
went out,
You were still holding
me.
I could see your
embrace.
But when I'm surviving, I can't
dream,
And so I haven't dreamt of yellow roads
with
Bright suns and flickers of hope buzzing
close,
Like fireflies in the
twilight,
Nor have I felt your embrace in
months,
Because someone stole
it.
Someone stole the
sun.

monkey bars

she fell
like a stack of
books, like
a star.
ankles
wrapped around
the ladder,
supposed to
ground
her, but
they leave her
breathless.

age eight.
life
knocked out
of her,
breath
reversed.

she wakes up,
fingers painted

red.
dead
space.

eight weeks.
softly
clutching what
isn't
there. her
heart breaks
like glass,
in
ferno,
in
firm,
clenched fists
she runs,
first –
born.

four foot

open wide.
let them see.
oak or maple?
maple.
maybe.
may I take a credit card?

making darling buds on treetops.
mailing invites
like sermons,
like circles,
all coming back

back then –
back when, all in
black then,
backing into a corner, baby,
back to the coroner, baby.

bury your feelings.
burn your flowers,
burden your family

with your grief,
with your teeth grit,
you lick sea salt off of coral reefs.

you try not to laugh like
U-boats sinking ships in the dark,
uniforms dyed red, no marks,
you want to cry but you laugh.
his tears are a part of you,
his teen years gone from you,
his too-wide eyes lost on you.

oak or maple?
aged like fine whiskey in some oak barrel,
pour maple syrup on pancakes, you are
aged with fine lines in the corner of your eyes
and he is never getting old.
oak.
let it soak in, baby.
he's never coming home.

winter on the isle of wight

snow falls, kissing the ground in
whispers of dandelion seeds.
in his oak old age,
his heart longs for a different song,
for a westerly wind,
for the tossing of salt waves –

when those who love him have left
with the changing of the wind,
no roots hold him stiffly to this ground.
they died with the winter;
but the sea births new life
with every crash against cliffs –

his fingernails are embedded in the crags
of this isle, in its rocks,
in the children and grandchildren
who leave like migrating birds
escaping the cold for spring-like air.
he is made from clay and chalk –

he leaves, in the morning,
the frost still clinging to the collapsing roots,
dew drops turned crystalline.
he lets blood and salt waves fill his lungs,
like wishes made on copper coins,
and heads west from Blackgang Chine.

Down Fulneck Beck

Standing at stiles in harvest heat, I've seen
Boys disappearing between the dark pines
That shadow the corner of the field. But
Of course there's more in it down there—
From well along the road, a drystone wall
Bordering the bare grass up to the woods
Where somebody had been and built a den.
I've seen it enough, though only passing by
On some days, when suddenly the trees bend
And let you glimpse the centre of the wood.
But being farther out of things and not a
Kid anymore, it's not how I remember it:
Roughing it in the wilderness between
Two towns, which hasn't been built on yet,
Should be simple enough. Unintruded
Unlike surrounding, suburban Wharfedale,
Somewhere out of the sun, that isn't seen.

Dark rings in the grass obscure the real thing.
And up in the branches, dust-sprung shadows
Overspreading the nettles and knotweed
Almost touch. Approaching in the long hours
One evening, I'd come with a folding saw
Curled-up in my coat—but that wasn't it.
Bending back down to the branch I cut down,
The den appeared, like a thought. So I went,
And bottles and binbags appeared as well.
Some plywood was used and stuck clumsily
Together with damp cardboard for a wall,
Save where it didn't match completely. And
The foundations slumped in a rough circle
Once it rained long enough. And inside it,
Burnt chairs and a stolen bench for a bed.
And above me the roof was almost gone.
In what's left of the bluish tarp though, torn
Out where it rested on a weave of rods,
There was a hole, thick as a thumb—through it
Feet shuffling on the horizon come to mind
As though someone's on pilgrimage tonight,
Going out to where there's another den.

Open Again

Our stories lie on sand now.
We open our shoes,
fill our blood socks with pebbles.
Stack of daily bread,
smacked with (strawberry) jam.

We open bras,
our chests,
throw our bodies into curly clouds combed into wavy blue.
We open our palms to find a compass,
but all we see are wrinkles of the sea.

Nothing is home.
Pearls walk out of shells
to be lost in the labyrinth
Or stolen by small nailed big hands.
Open the lacy curtains of the shell,
They don't peek,
they run.

Daarji's Photo Album

Shaw shook my belief in patriotism,
hence I could belong, but to myself.
And no one could paraphrase for me,
my grandfather's agony.

Never could I understand why Daarji would water his photo albums every Friday.
Until I found out his midnight cries weren't about patriotism or belonging to Pakistan,
They were about Bilal Ahmed.
All bedtime stories his coarse voice shared began with Bilal.

Bilal and I would read aloud Manto under Kikar trees
And hence I played a part in the play Toba Tek Singh.
Bilal and I would wear our fathers' white caps and kesri turbans and exchange them often,
looked handsome you know
And he dressed me up as a hippie on my fancy dress day.
Bilal and I delivered people's postcards,
Until we lost addresses.
So I decided to dig a tunnel for him.
When devils on earth's floor forbade love,
I decided to invade their land.
And I kept digging until my shovel
hit another shovel.
When the mud fell not to unveil more mud,
but a little boy in a white cap,
building a tunnel.

**Daarji* – Punjabi term to address grandfather
This poem was first published by Vayavya

Karan

His fingers touch laptop keys
as if playing a piano.
He gifts you ring-pulls, obsolete currency, old sweaters,
lends parts of himself to you,
but never asks for them back.
He is the sun in the colour of beetroot.
Whether on the rise or ready to set,
the sky around him shall always be in love,
crimson, crisp and beautiful.
He talks to birds,
in flocks and single,
and whispers in all of their ears,
their way back home.
And then,
he himself becomes a home.
The home you travel with and talk to every day,
the kind of home which doesn't inhabit you,
but the kind you store in your heart,
like the words of the first poem you ever read.

Guns and Flutes

Skin strolls into a hall of art,
whispers, heat, waiting.
Music soft-stomps minutes later,
and finally, the conjurer.
The maestro who helped these beat hearts
gather a purpose other than war.
Trained them to play bows and arrows
on their shoulders,
pistols straightened and put to their own mouths.
Trumpets, drums and horns retained,
just made
softer.

Showing us his back,
the commander then paints
with clear colours inside our eyes.
Without words, he writes, stories at once,
one per a pair of ears.
He dances with fingers, hands, head, hair
and demands the tune be created for him post.
Sometimes he plucks in the air,
throwing out the atoms that don't align with his sorcery.
Tosses to his army,
potions, glares and dry smiles.
He feeds us.
Leaves us with full bellies for days
and an aftertaste of running on a bridge.

We constantly worry for their stiff bodies.
But we forget they're soldiers
whose instinct is to hurt themselves to serve.
The guy with the French horn yawns.
Disinterested in war, disinterested in art.
By force of habit,
they wait for enemies
they wait for something to occur.
Drama doesn't need to unfold.
Everything happens, all the time

Symbolist Letter from Madrigal to Galahad

G –

A quick one to say: two things. No, I am alright. Getting on for ten o'clock, here it's so dull. Too long ago since you and I tore up the town. I wonder if – should I see you again, even. Every hour cannot be counted – you're quite the same.

Off topic – using the scientific method of pressing back my eye the pressure in my head abates. Am unable to tell if that is good. Not able to get a verifiable answer either. Do you suppose I'm not the only one? Tellingly, even the rats are leaving. Long gone most of them. Lost to dust and time.

You've missed my jests; only you would find that funny.

Underneath it all, I miss movement. Limbs and joints and such. Obviously I should not be gloomy. Very much trying not to be. Even you could be unhappy here.

You're very quiet these days. Obviously your reasons are good. Underwhelmed by life and missing everyone.

Best,
M

At night I see you and tell you I love you.

Galahad replies;

To; M

After dinner, read your letter. Reading it makes me miss and dislike you intensely. You are so flippant. Much could be made of the eye – even you must see that?

G

Marry me?

Green Willow

The body of the writer holds
more weight than the violinist.

He was worn so tightly you could play him.
“Music,” said one. “I could say it all with
music.”

But he couldn’t or didn’t. And that which we
have collected from the plains and Dales is

all the more archaic now for being taken.
It could have run its course, were it not a

museum piece; the body of the violinist not
weighing it down.

The Changeling

There's a wild girl living inside my head,
She reads me stories and screams me to sleep,
She lights fires and sings sweet sad songs,
She hides in lost things
And pounces.

She hurts like rain and cold and lonely madness,
But she doesn't understand why
She keeps running with spikes on her soles.

She stares with her gun barrel eyes,
Neither away nor at, only through.
She casts shadows on the wall at night
And lives off the beat of my fear.

She hopes one day to be a poet,
She says, she hopes she dies
When the tide is out so the moon can see.
She's got something wrong, I think,
Something a little lost about her,
She wishes we could live forever.

She leads us down paths we don't know
At night when no one can see,
There she teaches me faery dances
And teases the skin from my bones.

She saw you coming, she says,
Saw your eyes in some midnight, somewhere
Becoming real.
You set her eyes alight, and now

You're in love with the wild girl inside my head.
She dresses you in coal and briars, your blood runs
Through our veins as she drinks it full.
At night she sings soft sweet lullabies
And rocks you to sleep in my arms.

Empty Town

Watching whoever salvaged the earth bury the ruins
into the earth, like wiping away a name,
making the salvation of the menial
menial, before I want to excavate myself
I have nothing but history
outdated before felt.

Still, there are some days left
like morning mist wandering on the road
of early joggers. Sitting on an isolated rock,
I faced a yellow poppy, as if facing the key
to something I may desire.

But that kind of spring you wish to return to
is already autumnal. You retreat back inside the window
like a slice of the empty town.
Each year, the dying die onto the same soul.
The thrush pauses where spring cannot be deeper
and the old good time
begins to ferment in its own uselessness.

The futile garden has a futile man
when he sees me he becomes who I am.

The Master

An afternoon waking knocked over
a porcelain nap where I
had just become a Bodhi tree. Undoubtedly
the twilight borrowed my way for its way
across the imperial complex
a grain of pure dust on the sea-like bronze mirror.

Night dwelled around the attic of the temple spire
scrutinising me. I was memorising the fragments
of pagan sages, for the next morning debate
in the folded heart of the Grand Luminescent Palace;
it should be, let us say, about the wisdom of humble pride
or the language of the wordless.

Always keep in mind things that should not be there.
There, always.

Until incense-carriers increased there had been pigeons
that cared to loaf about.
A young monk held a handful of raw rice
up, when the sound of the bell brushed the sound of the wind.

I was old again
I told no one.

PROSE

Album of Written Photographs

Scarborough Shine

Written in Scarborough, England, June 2019

Who would have believed me if I'd told them the sun was currently roasting my ear as I sat on a pier in England? I certainly wouldn't have. English summers can be stubborn. Today is an exception.

A sailing boat gently floats towards the harbour. The sea seems to be relaxing its liquid limbs in the South Bay of Scarborough which has now turned into the familiar, playfully colourful town from the sketches and postcards.

Scarborough Castle has conquered the cliffs. It proudly divides heaven and earth as it outlines the headland. The sun is really roasting my ear – I have to turn.

The sea is now behind me, except for its glittering remnants in the harbour. It is unbelievable how many small boats there are, how many colours, how many masts, how much rigging.

St Mary's Church rests in the shadow of the clouds further down the hill by the castle. Just like the imposing fort, the little church sits on the horizon, but St Mary's holds heaven and earth together.

I turn back to the sea. Reflecting the sky, it finally gleams in fleeting flushes of aquamarine and all its shadows. The sea is enjoying the summer. It embraces the town. And sun-warmed Scarborough glistens in response. Scarborough welcomes the sea – keeper of a thousand currents.

A Beautiful Picture

Written in Weggis, Switzerland, August 2014

Pilatus is thinking. His head is veiled in thick white clouds. Slowly, they strive upwards, past the mountain, into the sky. Finally, the lake mirrors its blue. I wonder if ducks ever get sunburnt. Stop complaining, bird, I'm not doing you any harm! The black, duck-like sea-bird with its white cap is observing me suspiciously on one leg. My jeans are burning.

The small dock I'm sitting on is swaying gently with the waves. A band of four people provide the shore with a tawdry waltz. The swans gliding elegantly on the calm lake complement the picture perfectly. Postcard complete.

Suddenly, a white motorboat comes to a rattling halt at another dock. The old couple on it are fighting. He drove too far as she tried to get off and almost fell into the water. "Ja, härscht du nix?!"[1] she blusters. The music is as vivid as ever and thus brilliantly comments on the scene with subtle irony.

She goes to listen, he stays on the boat. The ducks are cleaning their wings. The bottom of the white boat is lit up with swiftly moving reflections of the edges of light on the waves. A beautiful picture, indeed. Postcard sent. Applause!

Roman Ruin Romance

Written in Schwetzingen, Germany, May 2019

The kingfisher looks up. Why has he not caught something? He angrily stares at the little brook, which is big for him. Other birds laugh – especially the crow. The water rushes down from the artificial ruin and you forget that the Romans were never here. An aqueduct is decaying perfectly, the ivy climbing just where it was told. A muskrat objects. It ravishes the lush green leaves. Now it busies itself mowing the lawn – well, someone has to do it. The shadows dance around me, as the sun twinkles through the trees. Like a tea-tray in the sky. Maybe we're in a postcard. The muskrat feasts. It is not impressed. The ruin is barely a few centuries old! Probably historically inaccu-rat. The Romans would be offended. The stones are much too pink anyway. But I think it's frozen Romanticism. History's attempt at historical art. Nostalgia become vintage. The muskrat eats a flower. The kingfisher is gone. But the sun still twinkles. It remembers.

1. Are you deaf?

The Blue Skylark

Written in Viareggio, Italy, September 2013

There's a ship at the horizon, balanced between sea and sky. Both of them patiently compete in blueness.

I can still taste salt on my lips. The sea has got the blues. She took it from me.

Slowly, the wind dries my hair, caressing my face with it. I don't look perfect now. Actually, I think I look rather bad, but I've never felt prettier. And this is all that counts to me. Finally.

I go closer to the water. Maurice gave me a cookie, and now its chocolate is melting in my mouth. For a moment, I think about dipping it into the sea. But the salt on my lips is enough to add the flavour of Tuscany.

Football is forbidden on the beach. 'What good will that do?' I'd like to ask the Italian sign, but I don't speak its language. The sea should take the sign away if it remembers its youth…

Hundreds of umbrellas in yellow, green, blue and white splash colours over the place. The glittering sea roars in a friendly way, opening freedom under the sky. The amount of space is overwhelming.

Giulio asks me to join the boys swimming. So I spread my wings.

In the Greenest

Written in Mannheim, Germany, April 2013

An owl screeches above my head. Is it the light of the clouds that makes the grass mirror the world? The lilac of little blossoms stands out against the green. They seem so witty in their sleep. The daylight doesn't waken them. When will the prince arrive to kiss them?

The wind twirls my hair. My knight is there in my sleep. Slowly he takes shape within my mind on the twirled meadow, as if the blades of grass were drawing him in the wind. Sparks of colour seem to be blown about.

I wonder how the meadow stays unstained. And as my knight takes shape, my shape he takes away and shields me from the rain.

Imagination is swift. We're but floating pictures. My knight and me on the meadow with the lilac blossoms and a tree. Wind. How small would we have to be to be sprung into the air by the fairy-like tips of the blades? Would Wendy need to sew our shadows to our feet? Or wouldn't we want our shadows back at all, Peter?

The raindrops will be so huge we'll see the future in them and we are so light we need no wings. The wind will carry us and the grass will make us jump to reach the clouds. And the clouds will drop looking glasses as we turn into fairies.

But what about the blossoms' prince? Will he come to shield them when we come falling down? Do the lilac blossoms have a mind to shape a prince?

The meadow sparkles as though it were smiling at me and my imaginary knight. What will he become in winter?

The lilac beams through the green. The grass is twirled by the wind. Beams glitter on frost.

Wharton Park in the Wind

Written in Durham, England, October 2019

The leaves are full of stories today. The wind gives them a voice that shrouds every other sound in mist. 'I know the place. I was here long before you,' rustles the tree behind Wharton. The sun lights up his wooden statue with a Midas touch. The sun sparkles onto my page through the branches of the trees. The leaves are full of stories today and eager they are to tell them. Below me they crackle past on small gusts of wind and a dog goes chasing them, increasing their crackling even more. The squirrel is a quieter fellow, barely visible against the grey path.

The wind blows my hair in the direction of the stories and they cover my view so I can hear the butterflies and fairies. When I shake back my hair I take in the view of the Cathedral before me. Magic and majestic, put there in front of us like a model house for little me to play with. The shadows dance in its ornaments and the wind carries the sound of knights and monks and dragons towards me. The shining armour rustles into the castle and the monks' feet patter into the Cathedral. The ghosts in these old buildings will not stay unheard. The dragon rumbles in the mountain on its back. The Cathedral embraces the sun because its fire is further away.

Brandish your shield, not your sword, little princess – a toddler hobbles my way. You will be a strong knight, keep your city one day. The leaves are full of stories.

Wither; Ruminate

It lay against the graffiti-covered wall of a disused walkway, glum and resentful, its composite planks fastened lazily together by several bands of rusted iron. It looked to me (I had, admittedly, only been in a boat a handful of times) as if it would just about float, at least upon the still canal by which it had been abandoned. That said, it gave off an air of dejected impotence that suggested it had entirely given up the will.

I couldn't quite say why I had stopped here, at this point on the route, this litter-strewn bend. It was, objectively, one of the least memorable sections of the walk, and I held no sentimental attachment or secret liking for the place. It was empty, I suppose. Hollow, downcast, grey, and it didn't look as if that would change any time soon. It suited the mood I was in; self-indulgent melancholy, precipitated by a morning peppered throughout by a number of forgettable disappointments, the kinds you wouldn't notice by themselves but, when suffered one after another, worked gradually to worsen your mood until you reached the state in which I now found myself. With some piece of appropriately sombre music playing quietly in my earphones (Mahler's Second Symphony, I believe, although perhaps it was something else), I sat down on a slightly damp bench, the only one I'd seen in the last ten minutes. Content in my discontentment, with nothing to do, no one to please or let down for the rest of the day, I set about taking in my surroundings, and found the dingy little boat to be the scene's most interesting character.

Its peeling paintwork must have once shone a vibrant green, its cracked window panes must have once acted as clear portholes for the cabin. Mould, rather than varnish, now coated the vessel, providing a clammy veneer that looked to be suffocating the wretched thing. Whilst trying to figure out why I was sympathising with it more than I thought warranted, a few lines from Emily Dickinson's 'I felt a Funeral, in my Brain' came to the fore in my mind (I had been recommended it only two days before, so it was fresh in my memory): "And mourners to and fro/kept treading - treading… and creak across my soul/with those same boots of lead, again". Something like that, at least. The dull monotony of leaden boots treading upon the decking

– to and fro, off and on, again and again. It felt almost a kindness to have it off the water and left to rot away, free from being worked to its creaking core, day in and day out.

From behind me, a child's voice cut through the low-pitched murmuring of a nearby A-road. The sound was that of play: a cry of reproach, a challenge, a whoop of victory. As I couldn't hear a response, I assumed that the child was either alone and caught up in their own excitement, or that an adult had answered in a slightly less animated manner.

Retreating back into my thoughts, and reflecting further on the words themselves, I wondered as to how much, of our vast canon of vaunted stanzas, was wholly true. Perhaps that did not matter. They had been said, and they had been received. The burden had been taken off the poet's chest, relieving her of the divine dissatisfaction that comes with leaving a piece unfinished; it was more the removal of a humming discomfort than the granting of any significant pleasure. We, in turn, had presumed to apply the words so precisely to our own lives that they now held some podium position of influence (and a certain kind of personal, incontestable truth), leading to the fostering of a unique relationship with the poet. One that had, by some miracle, surpassed any and all other resonances made by a previous audience.

Was it the duty of the poem to ring true? Or was it to ring *well*? To suggest to the reader that the language had somehow drawn itself up from the mire and taken form as verse, a result of some moment of revelation, the visitation of a muse, or the involuntary unpicking of some indeterminate psychological cipher, rooted in childhood, rather than the neat labour of two dozen nights in November, when we are teased by the hint of snow upon the earth. A taste of winter, pure and sweet, and yet dissatisfying, ever tinged with a dirty, urban warmth, the inescapable knowledge that this world is withering, gasping her final hundred ragged breaths as our sprawling masses eat away at her core. She lies suspended, meek and suffering, beheld by the unkind eyes of those other regal planets, as they emanate splendour and arrogance throughout the Milky Way:

towering, unassailable, unmarred. With life comes decay. With decay comes a greater appreciation for what has been, or will be, lost. I knew that, and yet thinking about a decaying earth filled me only with raw disgust, rather than any kind of cathartic pathos. Perhaps 'things' were most beautiful, in terms of their value, when they were dead. No, not dead, so much as distilled, free to be observed but not experienced. To romanticise a dead earth was misguided on two accounts.

It would be false to call Saturn, for example, "dead" in our sense of the word. Certainly, it could not harbour the life we have so quaintly engendered on Earth, but it performed an elaborate play of its own, a maelstrom of gas, ray and dust that silenced its audience, and projected a cosmic majesty quite surpassing Earth's. Secondly, how could beauty be perceivable without life? Of course, it was easy enough to *call* a dead thing beautiful, but I'm not sure I actually believed it. A gravestone certainly held a romantic poignancy, it embodied a time passed, a life grappled with, relationships made, and lost, but was there anything beautiful about the decomposing matter of the cadaver itself, locked in its earthen cage beneath the surface, hemmed around on all sides by soil, root and worm? About the incessant erosion of the headstone by microscopic specks in the air? Colliding, grinding, falling, rising, colliding. About the torrent of acid rain that would play about its marble face and dissolve the tablet to dust, until no one left existed to watch it? I didn't think so. Fascinating, depressing, inexorable, yes, but not beautiful, not romantic. The snow, the snow was romantic, and yet so often it disappointed.

From the right, a pair of pigeons edged closer to the bench, scanning the ground for food. The bolder of the two sported a gammy leg (perhaps reverence by the other for this war wound had led to its taking the lead). They regarded me with a wariness that suggested these were not high-street birds, but were not so flighty as to be scared away from the prospect of lunch. I felt bad for pigeons. They had this reputation as 'rats of the sky', denied the associations of grace and freedom we usually attach to birds, but had always seemed harmless enough to me; just *fine*, just *there* – perhaps ought to feel bad for rats.

But the snow, the woollen banks of snow, with its crackling wood fires, its heady mulled wine, its ruddy cheeks and itchy knitted jumpers, its Christmas. How could this collection of sharply cooled water, the water we curse and rue when it interferes with our meticulously arranged hairstyles, through mere mechanical metamorphosis, one temperature to another, transform in meaning and connotation to enchant us so wholly? It caused an ache within me to return to childhood. Whether that was because the world had been less wracked by the cancer of global warming, or because, back then, Christmas had provided the unbridled joy of gift-giving, gift-receiving, and the gathering of family, rather than the pragmatic pessimism December cast upon me now, I was unsure. During those times, when family got together, it was to celebrate life, to shelter you, let you bask in their company, and humour you by basking in yours. Time lasted longer then. Not a month, but a nine year old's month, imagine! Now, it seemed, family got together because it was the thing to do. It was scheduled and proper. Wonderful, in its own way, but it harboured no magic, failed to sustain the same untainted joy; no longer did peeking mystery lie under those frosted banks, waiting patiently to be coaxed out by childlike imagination.

Had this always been the case, I wondered, that we so readily idealise the past, exaggerating what has been lost beyond fair reason, and conveniently misremembering all that has been gained? It seems now so entrenched in our psyche to extol what has been, to raise it onto a pedestal and send it into the ring against what is to come, that we cannot help but mourn a past we have never observed. Those old gravestones, with their cracked, haggard faces and dull green skirts of lichen. Thinking of them conjures pastelled images of little village communities bustling about, divine in their charm and solemnity. They come together to bring in the year's harvest under a gentle sun, before settling down to quench their thirst with freshly brewed, pulpy cider at the local tavern, wherein they share stories, sup on hearty meals of bread and hard cheese, quiet crowds listening intently to the imparted wisdom of the old with the sombre, naive reverence of the young.

We think of meadow flowers and forests unconquered, of winding tracks trod by horse and cart, brooks that run pure and unpolluted – the hallowed sites of courtship and cradles of ancient folklore. We forget the hunger, the howling pain accorded to a family arising from what we might now think of as everyday illness, the nauseating fear that this winter might be the winter we run out of firewood and have our homes punctured by baying northern winds, our children dying in their sleep, comfortless and afraid.

How joyous it would be to venture back there, if only for a moment, and adopt their shining optimism about the future, as they perceived around them a breathing world, alive with myth. They had their problems of course, but, whatever their hardships, they at least did not have to come to terms with the fact they were complicit in the forced biological atrophy of their planet.

An aeroplane directly above caught my eye, coming into view close to the exact centre of my vision. I found it odd that I had seen it before hearing it, although it really was quite far away. I found it stranger still that real people were boxed inside that speck, incomprehensibly high up. Some of them were probably exhausted from the strains of travel, some excited to be visiting, others relieved to be coming back. I had always preferred watching planes at night, when they appeared as blinking dots on a star-painted radar. It had been a while since I'd been on a plane.

Blake, Wordsworth, Yeats. Yes, Yeats, with his rich folklore, his playful verse, his considered occultism. What would Yeats have thought to this vacant pessimism, the sullied, industrial outlook he fought so vehemently to resist; so dull, so abhorrent, and yet so fully, so insidiously pervasive. In days gone by, when you looked out past the coast, you saw nothing but sea for miles around. You *knew* there were countries at the other end of it: America, Spain, the faraway lands of Russia and Arabia, but you had no wealth of imagery or information upon which to draw, no irritating conceptions of international relations, warring politicians, oil prices. You saw merely opportunity, and were in full ownership of the pictures you painted, foreign lands acting as private canvases upon which to splash any tidbit of information you may have garnered from rumours, newspapers, novels and –

"... lighter on you?"

The speaker's words had come upon me unawares, jolting me out of my reverie.

"Sorry?" I turned to look at him now, scanning his face for any feature that I might recognise. My response was more a reflex than a genuine question; as I spoke the word I began to process what he had said beforehand.

"I, uh, was just wondering if you had a lighter." He performed a quick clicking motion with his thumb.

"Oh. No, sorry, I don't smoke." Blinking slightly, I still felt strangely unguarded, and was only beginning to ease back into the motions of ordinary conversation.

"Alright, no worries." He gave a faint smile, paused, then turned and walked away.

Looking back at that little green boat, it seemed no longer to hold the attraction it once had, so I decided to begin my own journey home and, zipping my raincoat right up to the neck, left it to its lonely vigil.

Bute

From the park, it's hard to believe you're in the city at all. Vast expanses of green stretch out in all directions, wildflower lawns meeting a heather-laden hill away in the distance. Gulls land among fallen blossom and yellowing leaves. Two neat rows of trees follow a path from the gate before diverging, the tarmac becoming no more than a worn trail, the wild countryside beginning. The river runs like a vein from the valleys. Here, it is still, interrupted only occasionally by a resting bird. In the summer, thumb-size dragonflies flit over its surface, creating ripples which grow to both riverbanks and then ebb quietly away.

The air is clearer here, tinged only with the residual scent of summertime pollen. Clouds drift over and announce their presence with the sharp, cold first drops of a Welsh storm. Umbrellas are deployed, hoods pulled up in preparation, but the rain doesn't quite arrive, and instead the clouds are swept briskly away by a firm, decisive breeze.

A woman wearing wellington boots watches her spaniel paddle at the water's edge, searching defiantly for a lost stick which has long since sunk to rest on the riverbed. She gazes at the confused dog through rain-spattered spectacles, trying to recall if there is still an old bitten towel in the car. A passing toddler points at the dog and is ushered away before she can attempt to join it in the water.

The tranquillity is deafening. Away from the traffic, the tourists, the turmoil, the quiet is out of place. The city's background sounds have been switched off. The park has a noise of its own – birdsong, the gentle muted conversations of passers-by, the shuffle of footsteps on drying leaves. Everything is painted in earth and amber. There is a circle of rocks just beyond the path, irregular and protruding from the ground at jutting angles. The miniature Stonehenge has been worn smooth by clambering children, forming a protective, spectral ring around a collection of pushchairs and colourful backpacks.

One child places a wrong foot on a precarious edge and tumbles into the long grass. Screams are averted with the infallible aid of a Chocolate Digestive and a dinosaur plaster over the superficial graze. Some of the other children crowd to watch this familiar ritual but most continue bounding between the rocks, unconcerned.

As the light fades, the people begin to filter out, some over the pebble-dash bridge onto the main road, others through the castle wall, many following the stream up to the rugby playing fields and out to the edge of the city. The river is wider here, with shallow banks which slope gently into clear-running tributaries and eventually to the murky green of the deepest water. The trees loom from both sides, willowy branches trailing into the river. Wood smoke winds delicately through the branches from a small fire on the Western bank, and a line of chimneys puff more from the houses beyond.

Kicking through the shallows, a young couple forms a neat romantic silhouette against the setting sun. She watches the darkening skies over the university halls and he watches her. Bedroom lights begin to flicker on before them, several thousand students coming home and getting ready for the night ahead. Blinds are drawn. A cool breeze washes over the couple as they wander, sleep-like, towards the rising babble of voices.

The shadow of the city's tallest tower falls over the trees in the evenings as inside its lights fizzle into life. In the night, the park is alone, gates locked. White moths flutter like snowflakes in the hazy half-light, dancing around the delicate bare branches of deciduous trees. The ferns by the garden walls rustle insistently in the rising wind, a sudden chill descending over the city like a blanket. A silver moon materialises, occasionally dipping back behind the shade of passing clouds, white light illuminating their outlines. The warm glow of urban streetlights blocks out the scattered stars visible from the countryside beyond.

A shuffle in the undergrowth is succeeded by a yawn. One corner of a battered sleeping bag pokes out into the open as its owner readjusts his position. He watches shadows move across the violet sky through gaps in the trees and ignores the occasional drops of rain, pulling his hat down over his ears as he waits for sleep. In the morning, he'll move before he is found.

Before anyone else is awake, he shuffles out of his hiding spot, swings his bag over his shoulder and moves towards the castle entrance and the city centre. A jogger takes advantage of the early light and follows an intricate path spanning most of the park before conceding that it's time for work. She deftly changes direction and heads towards the city, passing the corner of a sleeping bag without noticing it.

Blue Moon

I am watching my son through a mirrored window from the fifth floor of the office building I own. He is standing in line with someone to see *Mission Impossible III*, which is playing across the plaza from where I work. He keeps looking up at the window I am standing behind. I'm on the phone with Saunders and he's talking about the finalities of a deal we worked on last week even though I'm not listening to him.

I stare through the glass, relieved that Jacob can't see me, that we can't share a wave. He and his friend just stand there waiting for the line to be let in. His friend – I think his name is Sam or Michael or something – looks a lot like Jacob: tall and dark-haired and pale, both wearing loose jeans and red-and-blue T-shirts with the sleeves rolled up. Jacob raises his eyes to the window again. I put my hand to the surprisingly cool glass and hold it there. Saunders says that he'll be on the business retreat with Davis and Bradford, and asks if I'd like to join them on their fishing weekend. I tell Saunders that I'm taking Jacob to Lake Foster for four days. Down below, Sam or Michael whispers something in Jacob's ear. Sam/Michael's movements and subsequent grin seem odd to me and I can't place why.

Saunders says maybe he'll talk to me after I get back from Lake Foster. I hang up, taking my hand off the window again, thinking about the time three years ago when I took Jacob to Hawaii for part of the summer break. I remember how, when we got off the plane, a pretty, sweet-faced Hawaiian girl put purple leis around our necks and said, welcome to heaven. Olivia calls from her desk, says that Richard Matthison is on line two, and I tell her I'm not here and I stand at the window and watch Jacob and Sam/Michael until long after the queue goes in and Jacob disappears through the lobby doors. When I leave the office early, around four, I'm in the underground parking garage, fiddling with the keys, and I loosen my tie and check my eyes in the rearview mirror, and then I'm driving away, out of the city, and onto the next part.

In the car on the way to Lake Foster, Jacob fidgets with the radio and can only find a local station playing old seventies songs. I take my eyes off the road and look over at Jacob as The Zombies begin to sing 'Time of the

Season'. He just sits there, white headphones hanging limply around his neck, his blank eyes staring out the tinted windows, looking over the sweeps of green land. He has a magazine clutched in his hands, rolled tightly into a periscope, and I ask myself if this is the right thing to do. Jacob glances over at me and I avert my gaze and an imagined sense of imposed peace washes calmly over the two of us, answering my question. I turn up the volume of the radio.

Three years ago, when we were on the flight to Hawaii, I remember how I asked the stewardess for a deck of cards and Jacob and I played a few games of Snap and Cheat and he won all four games. Later, Jacob watched a movie whilst I looked out at the great expanse of sea below us, and I thought about what it would be like to float in the ocean with the moon beaming down on me. Jacob rolled around in his sleep and murmured something about feeling upset and angry at how things were going. Under his breath, he said, we are heading for super dark times. He woke up and I asked what he had been dreaming about. He said that it was a nightmare, but he couldn't remember the specifics. We landed in Hawaii, and all I saw for the next week were dark omens.

Jacob and I are sitting in the main dining room at the Dawson East Inn. The dining room has one wall that is open, and I can hear the far-off sounds of people walking along the pier. A breeze enters the darkened room, the flame of the candle at our table flickering for a moment. A gentleman at the piano plays some upbeat chords while two elderly couples dance awkwardly in the darkness. Jacob looks away, folding his arms, too tired to be embarrassed. I ask him if he wants another drink and he directs his answer to the empty table next to us. A woman's laughter drifts through the large dining room, leaving me, for some reason, clueless.

I ask Jacob how his friend Sam is doing. Jacob stares at me and tells me he doesn't know anyone by that name. I consider trying another name, but can't decide which one to try. I shrug, looking away. I suggest we go to the bar, and Jacob gets up quickly.

At the bar, I spot two well-dressed women in their early thirties sitting together. I nudge Jacob, leaning towards him conspicuously, and ask what he thinks of the women, grinning madly. Jacob looks at me irritably, looks at the women, and flinches. When the bartender comes back, I get him to send a couple of drinks to the women, who begin to giggle amongst themselves.

A little while later, they come and sit next to me and Jacob. I ask them where they're from and what they're doing at Lake Foster. They laugh and answer my questions and give darting glances to Jacob, unsure as to how they're meant to engage him in the conversation. I tell them that my son is an economics student. One of them asks Jacob where he studies. It takes him almost half a minute to answer her question. The three of us stare at Jacob like he's some kind of blank, exotic creature, more stunned than we should be by how inarticulate he actually is. He keeps shaking his head slowly… Eventually, he mutters 'fuck you' under his breath and says that he's going to the toilet, walking out of the bar and towards our room. I sit with the women for another ten minutes or so before things become uncomfortable and they leave too. I stay at the bar for another hour, waiting for Jacob to come back, but he never does. I finish my cognac and survey the room one last time.

I wake Jacob early and tell him we're going to play tennis before breakfast. He gets up easily, without protest, and takes a long shower. After he gets out, I tell him to meet me down at the courts. When he gets there, fifteen, twenty minutes later, I decide that we should warm up, hit a few balls. I serve, slamming the ball forwards. He misses it. I serve again, this time harder. He doesn't even try to hit it, ducking instead. I serve again. He misses it. He doesn't say anything. I serve again. He hits the ball back, grunting with exertion, tumbling forward.

"Not so hard, Dad," he says.

"Hard? You call that hard?"

"Well, uh, yes."

I serve again. He doesn't say anything. After I've won all four sets, I try to be sympathetic. "You win some, you lose some."

Jacob says, "Sure."

We take a walk along the pier, looking at the boats. Jacob has a pair of dark sunglasses perched on his head, keeping his hair back. We both turn our attention at the same time to the loud family a little way behind us. Jacob stares, wondering, and puts his sunglasses on.

I find us some deck chairs and suggest we sit before we head to lunch. Jacob shrugs, looking behind him. At some point I go to the toilet, spotting the women from the bar from the previous night, and I instinctively keep my head down and move quickly on. When I come back, I find that my chair is now being occupied by a young woman in conversation with Jacob. I stand at a distance and quietly observe. Their heads are both bent over in grave consultation. Jacob points to something out on the lake, looks back at the young woman, and raises his eyebrows. The young woman nods sternly. They both suddenly break into laughter. I notice that Jacob looks more relaxed, his shoulders slackened and his gaze direct. The young woman stares piercingly back at him. In a swift moment, she shakes her head, laughs once more, and leaves the deck chair, waving absentmindedly at Jacob. He waves back, and as she walks away I watch his face tighten and compress.

Later, after the beach, we are both in the bathroom getting ready for dinner. Jacob has a towel wrapped around his waist while he shaves. Without embarrassment, he takes the towel off, and wipes foam off his jawline.

He asks me if it's okay if he meets Carolyn after we have dinner. I ask if she's the girl he was speaking with this afternoon. Jacob looks at me, briefly bewildered, but quickly regains his composure. He says yes. I put on a linen suit and pour myself a drink from the minibar and sit on the bed, watching Jacob put gel in his hair.

"Are you glad you came?" I ask.

"Sure," he says evenly.

"I thought maybe you didn't want to come."

Jacob pauses. "Why would you think that?"

"Your mother mentioned that you didn't feel like coming," I say, too quickly, so it comes out wrong. I sip my drink.

He looks at me in the mirror, his face unreadable. "No, I never said that. I just had this essay I had to do and, um, I don't know."

He combs his hair, inspecting himself. Satisfied, he turns away from the mirror and I'm confronted with this man of mine, with the face I know I made. Now I'm unsure whether it still belongs to me, and whether it ever did. Jacob fixes me with that blank stare, his eyes boring holes into my retinas, until all I'm left with is empty sockets, craters where my eyes used to be.

After dinner, I wander around the grounds of the inn for a long time and finally end up sitting on a small bench next to the lake, next to a floodlight shining down into the water. I look out at the lake, stretching out like a flat black sheet. Looking up into the night sky, I notice that the moon is high and dull and pale. It looms over me. I hear footsteps, and then Jacob arrives and quietly joins me on the bench, feeling and knowing something I don't. We both stare blankly at the largeness of the big blue moon hanging above us as we hurtle through the vastness of space, shifting in and out of each other's orbit.

Rainbow states

I used to sit in the station wagon while Papa made deliveries. That's what Papa told me, and he told me not to be making no more questions out of it, that he done told me before, that all I had to do was sit tight in the back carriage. If cops or creeps came, I was to hide under the blankets in the back where we slept on the move, and only honk if they stopped and started prowling.

I normally flipped to Side B of our tape for them times when Papa were busy. I'd borrowed crayons from a diner to sketch a rainbow over that side one day, and that had made it for me. When Papa seen it, he'd looked hard and long, and sad, I think, but he said nothing. I didn't get what the big deal was. This here's mine, that's what I thought.

TRACK ONE on the list was *Summertime*, Ella Fitz and Louis Armstrong, then Nina, Whitney, Michael J, the King... Papa called them all classic. He laughed that it was the softer stuff he liked to listen to sometimes. Papa said any music that didn't have real beat was soft, and as long as it stayed quiet "like them mouses" while he was gone, and I weren't too loud, I were allowed to listen to what I wanted. I'd put it on, and by the time Ella's voice swung into my ears like a lullaby, and Louis' deep Cookie Monster tones rumbled in, I'd forget about the blackness pressing firm against the car windows.

Papa had parked us up on a dirt track opposite the motel between two steep wooden fences that hid the car off from the rest of the street. I'd been dozing when we pulled in, so I hadn't seen what was on either side of them, but they only made the darkness more solid, gripping the wagon from three sides. Behind me was the night, and in front of me the motel—tinted by red neon like it were still stuck at sunset.

I had my drawing pad spread across the back carriage when I heard a shout from the road, over the tape. Papa was returning through the dark, a black cutout from the bright motel, the front of him lit dimly by the only working streetlight half a block away. Shirtless, he blended mostly into the night—said this was his special hiding trick, like how I had a special name I could still blend in with—but I could see that he were real angry.

"*Weh,* fuck you man, you got what you paid for. I ain't gonna go for no more," Papa shouted over his shoulder, but he smiled when he saw me—bright teeth in the dark—slapped the hood and jerked his finger to tell me to get in the front. Some man was running after him, panting before he even reached the road, white as a sheet, wearing a tank and some beige slacks. I'd got myself into the passenger seat, leaned over to turn the engine on as Papa done taught me, and did up my seatbelt before he was sliding into his seat and slinging his bag in the back. He quickly scanned my seatbelt with his shiny dark eyes then zipped up his loose jeans and buckled his own. Papa tripped the headlights on and they burst onto the scene, blinding the man as he got closer. He shielded his eyes with his hands, huffing as he stepped forward, pleading with Papa to cut a deal, that he thought men like him were good all night. When he got close enough to see me, wrapped up in my sweatshirt in the passenger seat, his eyes widened. I could just about hear him muttering outside the wagon.

"Oi, fuck, that there a kid you got?" he wheezed. I was no kid, and I stuck out my tongue at him as Papa revved the engine and surged sharply forward, the white man leaping out of the way and landing in the filth where the sidewalk met dirt. I noticed he were still barefoot.

"Fuck you!" Papa screamed as we pulled away.

"Fuck you!" I screamed, and we were steady hollering till we were nearing the highway again and our lungs were left breathless.

*

"Mikhuul, you gonna choke if you don't sit up."

Papa named me Mikhuul after the King. He said he were a bit on the soft side—the music, not me—but he liked it anyway. As far as I cared, if something were alright with Papa it were alright with me.

I was slumped beside him, my sneakers braced against the dash to keep the peeling soles together, and the seatbelt high up on my chest like them nooses Papa told me about. We'd been driving in silence since the music cut out, and I heard him say my name but kept my eyes on my drawing pad.

I weren't allowed to stick stuff up any place, not in the car or on any motel wall, but the pad itself, that there was mine. I filled it with everything I couldn't even dream of having.

"I'm a-gonna take that pad off you." Papa flicked his gaze between the quiet highway and the words I put on the page. "What's that?" he scoffed as we drove fast down the open road. He laughed a little but there wasn't much to see out there in the dark. "You *crazy*, shit, what do you know about pussy, you know nothing boy. Show some respect."

The streetlights were paced out like a beat, a light rhythm scoring the wagon, bright white then dark on repeat. I turned the page over. Under the lights, Papa's sharp gaze returned from the road to me. A few seconds passed, then he pointed. "What's that word supposed to say? About Harry Potter?"

"Picture." I rolled my eyes, though we were moving through darkness again then. "What it look like Papa?"

"Ah, aight," Papa said. He shook his head, then he laughed again like he were remembering some joke. "I thought Harry Potter were a year or two too old for you."

"No it ain't. It don't matter. And it's got pictures. And just 'cause I'm a slow reader, don't mean I'm slow."

Papa grinned. "You my boy, man. I'm gonna buy you some real shit one of these days, Mikhuul, you get me?" he said. "Do you understand?"

"Yeah, Papa."

He been trying to raise me to sound more decent than he ever had—that's what he always said—but he always forgot about following through. What was wrong with the way we talk anyway? The real magic's in putting words down right.

"Aight, aight, how about this rhyme then," he said. "Give me a beat, little man." And I did. The dash became a drum that I thumped with my sneakers, and I beatboxed them sounds with my mouth that made it sound just like a real beat. Boom, boom, boom. Pop.

"I ain't too ga-ga-ghastly. I wanna see my face in a picture book. Gonna be the truth Harry, 'cause y'all be looking deathly shallow when I step up on the quidditch court..."

I kept the beat going. I loved it when we made music like this, and when we weren't making it, we were moving to it—or watching it. The two of us were a crowd around Papa's cell phone screen, like little lightning bugs around a streetlight, Papa's locks against my ear.

"This important Mikhuul, pay some attention," he would say so I'd watch closely. "This is *you*, this where you come from, don't forget." He'd tickle me then till I was squealing. "Don't forget."

*

When we pulled into the next motel, this one tinted by a big blue sign saying 24/7, Papa got a new shirt and "his shit" out of the trunk and we set in. The small parking lot was lit like one of them big storms we seen over Austin—Aquafina filtered through a motel ice-machine. It made the place seem dreamlike, a waking dream so real it feels like it's shot in HD, and not like somewhere made for people, like us.

While Papa got us a room, I sat outside on a park bench that turned out to be plastic. Above me, a VACANCY sign flashed like a cop car. The tape sat beside me in case the room had a box, something these lost places had sometimes, and my pad and diner crayons sat on my lap. An old white creep was there on another bench, all tanned and wrinkled, but I paid him no mind. I'd seen some men like that before and they always had a banjo or something. That ain't cool.

There were some white kids too. Three of them came from around the corner, just as I was signing my name on the bench in black crayon, and looked at me, looked me up and looked me down, said:

"What's with your name?"

"That's not how it spelled."

"How comes *he's* darker than you?"

He—Papa—came out then and sent them nasties running. "How come *you* so much *uglier* than your Ma and Da?" he called after them. "He ain't got time for you, *shit*."

"Fuck you!" I hollered, and we chased them away with our laughter. Who the hell they think they is?

The old white man spoke up then. Looked my Papa up and down and said, "You got good time right there."

"How's that?" Papa said, turning on him.

The old man snorted like a mad thing, "Don' nobody want whatever you tryna push here."

Papa bristled. "I'm not working no trap. And I'm not no plug," he said slowly. "Sir."

The man ignored him, squinted at me as if seeing me for the first time, crow eyes sunken deep beneath his brow. He had that gaunt type of wrinkledness, paper crumpled up and flattened out again, that made him look like something long dead. He looked at the tape beside me.

"You some kind of queer?"

I thought Papa was going to clock him then, put him down like a dog, like I'd have done if I were bigger, but instead he said, calmly, "He's no faggot. He's just a kid."

"You're barely a kid yourself ain't you, nigger."

*

Papa ignored all my questions till we were in our room, and then he only answered one. "Why don't you ever say that Papa—*nigga*?"

"'Cause I don't want you be saying it," he said in that tone that meant: "Don't you be making no more questions out of it." But he added, "Don't just see what they want you to see, Mikhuul. Don't let 'em."

I sat on the bed and Papa came by me and unzipped his bag. He threw something into my lap. A wallet. "Here, take a look of this,' he said. The thing were already emptied of money, but inside there was a photo of the man from earlier, standing in front of a big house and trees with a woman and two kids littler than me. A slim blue license read NEW YORK STATE across the top. It seemed a million miles away to me.

Papa made a good haul. When he made a delivery to one of them fancy motels with the "free shit", we always made it big. Papa and me had always done it that way—he finessed his way in on one of them sites or apps or something and then we made it up. We made it up like we came up in a castle.

I spotted that he were putting money aside every delivery. He said things would be "better" for me, that I'd never have to do deliveries, but I were alright. He said we never had to want for nothing but, when food was short, it were always him that went hungry first. He teased that he liked it like that, that he was fattening me up for a big meal one day, tickling me and baring big monster teeth. I knew he'd never hurt me for real. I knew it like I knew the road never ended and that Side B came after A.

After we ate—candy bars, Twinkies, Lay's, "garbage" vending machine popcorn, soda—Papa said he was tired and it were time for bed even though the room had a TV. He was feeling *"kagou"*. He had good days and bad days "just like everyone else". I thought it'd been a good day, but maybe it hadn't, which meant at least that I could watch TV that next morning.

When we stayed in special motels like this, with a TV, and Papa were tired and needed to sleep extra-long, he'd let me watch cartoons all that next morning. I never knew if he were really asleep, 'cause when he really was his breathing would turn to snoring and he'd toss and turn. But, on these days, sometimes, he'd lie completely still and quiet in them darkened little rooms, facing the peeling walls as the little TV threw flashing lights across them, red, white, and blue.

Unbelonging

'I don't know what it's like to come from a place that doesn't make you sad,' she said.

Chris raised an impatient eyebrow.

'I think we Cypriots are all born into a state of unacknowledged misery, a vulnerability embedded in our collective subconscious.' She felt flames lick her cheeks as she went on. 'I'm here, and we're having this conversation, but I don't feel like you know me.' She stared at the carpet – dark blue with thin lines running through it, an arbitrary pattern evidently intended to cover up its flaws, barely visible stains.

Chris stared at her. 'But,' he suggested, with some effort, 'you haven't actually lived through any of it. So how can it be?'

She shook her head. 'It's part of who I am. It's biting into my heart.' She gave him a wild look – 'I am fully aware this sounds dramatic, but it's true. I mean it!'

Chris welcomed this small concession – he got up, quickly circumvented the coffee table between them, and sat down next to her on the sofa.

'What I don't understand,' he said, eyes a little too humble, thought Sophia, as he extended his hand to take hers, 'is what this has to do with us.'

She kept her hands around her mug, as if to draw warmth from the cold coffee in it. 'It has everything to do with us. Well, mostly it's got all sorts of everything to do with me, but that does mean it's got something to do with us. I can't make that change. Don't you get that?'

He leaned back, withdrawing his hand. There was a flash of hardness in the way he looked at her. Impatience. 'No,' he said. He coughed and looked away, regretting joining her on the sofa – a small defeat. 'I can't believe you're breaking up with me over… well, what even is it? Politics? History? The state of the world, essentially. Evidently I'm not doing a great job restoring cosmic order – need to work on that.' It was *his* cheeks that were burning now.

Sophia put her mug down on the table. 'Well, this is gonna go great places,' she sighed, averting her gaze.

'I just can't believe you can be so *casual* about it.' He considered other words, better words to voice his anger, betrayal, shame with, but he wasn't going to be cruel. He felt them both standing at the cusp of a melodramatic telenovela argument, but he had no interest in or patience for that. There were things he could say that he wouldn't mean, that would fall between them like heavy boulders, a bulldozer demolition. He said none of them. Chris preferred to walk away from standing things.

Sophia pulled her phone out of her pocket and played a Greek song. 'There,' she said. 'Do you understand that?' She knew she was going too far – she was becoming absurd and now he got to be reasonable. She still meant it, at the risk of rudeness and absurdity.

'Bullshit! Of course I don't understand it. Sue me for not being a Greek speaker.'

'It isn't bullshit to me.'

'Hi guys! How's it going?' Emily, who lived on the same floor, walked in in her dressing gown and slippers. They both said hi. Sophia turned to her phone.

Those silent nights / Athens will light up / like a great ship / that you'll be on too.

If Emily found the sad Greek harmonica song strange she didn't show it, just walked over to the tiled section of the room that acted as the communal kitchen and put the kettle on.

'We're just taking a break,' said Chris. 'How's your essay coming along?'

You will not miss me / for my soul's going to be / the song of the desert / following you.

They made meaningless small talk until she left with a cup of tea two minutes later. Chris turned back to Sophia, who let her phone fall on the sofa.

'So, suddenly I can't know you because I don't understand your Greek song, is that what you're saying?'

'It's not just the song. It's a feeling. A culture.'

'And it doesn't occur to you that maybe if there are things about you I don't know, it's because you never wanted to share them?'

Sophia shook her head. 'You couldn't understand,' she said, her voice sounding like it was on its tiptoes, careful not to lay too much weight on each word. He resented that.

'Try me.'

She was about to insist that it was pointless, but saw that he was serious about it. 'Fine,' she said, picking up the mug and taking a sip of cold coffee. 'Fine.'

He couldn't tell why she sounded so sad.

* * *

Sure, she hasn't lived through any of it. But being surrounded by people who have, one way or another, comes close. It's a sad country I'm from, she says.

So many visitors seem oblivious to the fact that, in her hometown, if you look to the north, there's a huge Turkish flag staring down at you from the mountain. It's there, seeping into the pores of your thoughts. She can picture the flag flashing at night over the highway back to the city, complete darkness for a moment, then – He-llo, it seems to say in perversely festive repetition. He-llo.

Imagine seeing that every time you walk your dog. 'I wish this was fiction,' she says.

Her eyes are set on the coffee table in front of them. She says she feels so conflicted. That even as she says all this she feels like a hypocrite, because she grew up safe. But it all feels borrowed. A borrowed safety, dependent on forces she can't name or understand.

She looks at him blankly – 'But then again I suppose all of life is borrowed safety.'

She says as a child she used to be frightened the Turks would invade Cyprus again. She remembers being seven years old and thinking, what will I take with me if the Turks come at night? She remembers the small backpack, her intention to grab it and throw in all necessities if they had to leave. Necessities being, she chuckles, her treasured books and lucky pebble and plasters, and her torch and compass of course.

When the news said Turkey invaded Syria recently, she was afraid. Last night, she tells Chris, I had a nightmare Cyprus was invaded again. There are maps going around crazy corners of the internet where Cyprus and Syria are painted red, captioned 'we will take back what is ours'.

She doesn't expect the people who surround her here to know or care, but knowing that the news didn't tug at their hearts this morning leaves her unstable on her feet.

'Why didn't you wake me up?' he asks.

'There was no point. I read you the headline earlier, but it didn't mean anything to you, and you didn't seem to think it meant anything to me.'

'You could have told me.'

She shrugs, guilty, then not.

She says her friend's grandparents, 82-year old refugees, still dream of the house they left in 1974. 'I asked him if they would bother moving back at this point if they were offered their house back. He looked at me kind of breathlessly, shocked that I would be so stupid.' She blushes.

'I was on a village bus last year on the anniversary of the invasion. The radio played a song about it and the people who died, and the old man next to me cried in silence for ten minutes while looking out the window.'

She hasn't lived through conflict. But the aftermath of what she hasn't experienced still permeates her life. So much of this is still ongoing.

'Take the queen,' she says. The queen whose grandson they'd watched get married on TV. Sophia had cried because he looked radiantly embarrassed and happy. Ellie had said 'Bless, the queen is such a cute old lady!' Sophia hadn't said anything but was thinking that this was the same queen who'd signed the execution order of her friend's grandma's brother. She was a young queen then, but the length of her reign spans the entire independence of Cyprus.

Her great-grandmother had a picture of Queen Victoria in the small house in the village where the sun lines the garden with negatives of vine leaves. These were realities hard to reconcile.

Chris shifts in his seat, but his gaze doesn't waver, and she likes him for it.

Outside the sun comes out, but this room faces north, and shapeless shadows lurk still on the walls.

Last year, she says, when they studied postcolonialism, she sat in that seminar feeling displaced. 'I am white,' she says, 'but Other.' The stuff she read to research her essay talked European colonisers and non-European colonies. 'I'm both. I am Europe and "the Levant".' Her people's whiteness saved them from worse things, but not colonialism. They weren't white enough to be worthy of independence.

She says she can't stop thinking that if her extended family was to walk through a room at their university, they'd read as Arabs. Dark, hairy, possibly loud. Her primary school class photos look Middle-Eastern too: big, dark eyes.

She says people like to forget. Cypriots pretend they were never colonised. They take books written about Cyprus by occasionally literary-minded colonialists and proclaim them masterpieces 'capturing the essence of the island' because, among the misogyny and racism, they offer pretty descriptions of Cypriot sunsets.

'There's still British bases in Cyprus, you know – that's where they bombed Syria from. I used to eat my cereal thinking that missiles were flying over my head.'

'My first week here,' she tells Chris, 'Mark declared that "Cyprus should still be a British colony," then laughed. He told someone else he didn't *really* mean it but just "liked to provoke".' So he meant it?

This isn't buried hatred, she says. She promises. She's perfectly aware history is not a victimhood competition, and even if it was there are other Others who have suffered more. She also knows little people have nothing to do with all this, that Chris himself has no say in his country's history, that he is not the embodiment of colonialism, that it isn't his fault no one knows about Cyprus still being illegally occupied, that this all sounds irrational and dramatic. But still.

It is an uneasiness. A knowledge of unbelonging. A surface. An identity crisis, political and personal.

The worst, she says, is feeling complicit. She thinks in English. She writes in English, too, as if she doesn't trust her own people to understand her, as if she isn't interested in their readership, as if it's less worthy. She uses the coloniser's language.

Ellie said to her in September that she'd visited Cyprus over the summer. 'The North part,' she'd said.

'You mean the illegally occupied area that your own country and the UN condemn and refuse to recognise as a state,' Sophia had said. A missed beat.

Ellie had chuckled. 'I suppose so.'

***

She looks at Chris.

'I don't know how to reconcile any of this with being happy with someone who knows and experiences none of it,' she says.

He doesn't know what to say, or what's worth saying. He dislikes her a little for opening a window into ugliness.

They are both aware they could reach over and hug. They know that in that moment it might be possible to erase the invisible line between them.

Neither of them moves, or says anything.

Dear Zoya,

Today is a new beginning. Look into the mirror; tease and slow-dance, strip, one button unbuttoned with each carefree sway. Come undone. This caramelised silhouette, this likeness of God, she can't be ugly.

Peer into the mirror with glassy eyes and count your countable eyelashes. A hundred something wet, sticky, and pretty strands press against each under eye.

But you can't freeze in time and stay the same. Beauty is only stagnant in things that don't change. Like life-like paintings. You, on the other hand, are alive. You breathe. You age. Chemicals turn your hair auburn; a straightener takes your electrocuted frizz and flattens it into obedient strands. A tiny razor cuts and sweeps the baby hairs away from your face. A colossal one with 5 blades smoothens your legs. A moisturiser softens your skin and you shine. Clothes hang in the right places to flatter your body. Earrings and rings and perfume spritzes and a red lip later, you look how you look.

Yes, you're not on a stage and there's no spectator watching your life unfold. Yet, you never question if there's a point in doing all that. You know that your beauty is just a cover-up for the messiest mess that happens under your skin.

Deep under your skin, you dreamt a little nightmare. Purple fireflies, illume inside an emptied rosé bottle. You held up your hand and his palm grazed against yours. Your long fingers felt short against his. There was someone with hands longer than yours! You stamped it as a perfect moment. And then he opened his mouth and spewed, "Men with big fists have big dicks."

Go shower and wash him off.

Not again. Not today! You won't play this dream again. Please. Do something phenomenal. Play Angus and Julia Stone's *Draw Your Swords*, put on mama's molten golden saree, add a hint of rouge to your lips, and flick your hair in front of a full-length mirror.

Or, go have an orgasm. Yes, on your own. You know *Tinder* didn't work out. *Tinder* only traced untraceable patterns on your skin for a second and shoved himself in and out of you in a blink. And you surely don't want to give *PlentyOfFish* a try.

Or text the known stranger from the club? Your thoughts had branched out wild, without ends. So, you wanted closure from his mouth, to questions raised by another of his kind. But club man was only yours for a night. Would he respond to your message? He must be busy swiping left and right to find his next muse. Maybe she'll come with long legs and a bubble butt.

Or imagine that you were a mermaid in your past life. Did you cry pearly tears like Shim Cheong did in *Legend of the Blue Sea?* Are those parts of you are still out there, adorning some old gran's neck?

Or take Terra's advice and bungee jump to get a thrill. But if you do, your boobs, teeth and hair will detach and fall off and you'll faint and hang mid-air like a floppy fish.

No. Think of hugs full of sunshine and warmth and magic. Or long fingers over a piano, playing a tune you can't quite remember. Or colours that make you happy. Or old lovers holding hands during their park stroll. Or babies and their button noses. Or clothes! You love clothes. Balenciaga and Dior stay on the floors above and below yours, and you frequently take bus rides with Gucci and McQueen. You breathe the same air and go to the same uni. But your realities are separate and isolated from each other with borders of their own.

Come back to reality. But what even is reality? It's a walled place with a gate and a gatekeeper who only allows non-loonies in. You wait for him to open the doors for you. You stand outside until you freeze and die.

You're not whole. You've assembled yourself from scraps. But hush. Just sing yourself a morbid lullaby. Billie Eilish's *idontwannabeyouanymore*.

Do fun things. Go skinny dipping until your lips taste like the waves. Have an espresso instead of a cappuccino. Scrape the crumbs from the bottom of the cookie jar and eat them. They taste better than whole cookies anyway. Learn Spanish beyond *Es un elefante*. Hang upside down from the edge of your sofa and play your Spotify playlist: *songs that have the word fuck*.

There's only ash in your mouth. But where did it all start? How did this happen? What did you do? You listened to Schmuck's narratives about other girls. Sexualised leg and breast and butt talks. Of brown girls and white girls and who's better in bed out of those two categories. You sat through all that until you were that girl.

He told you multiple times to remind him to keep a sweatshirt at your place. "It gets chilly while going back", he said. You really wanted that sweatshirt in your house, didn't you? You were taught how to connect the dots on paper and trace patterns in Kindergarten. But you failed to implement your education in real life.

There had been many comments here and there that you should have noticed. You should have, you could have, but you didn't. The way he spoke about other girls, how he told you, 'Give me a call in a few years if we are both still single.' It was him bookmarking you into a dating slot if he ever ran out of prettier girls. Thinking and planning ahead.

You sat with a bag of lacy lingerie and a box of red velvet cookies only to be told over a text that it was over. Had anything even begun? He slithered out of his skin as a man-child. A fuckboy-non-friend.

Cry in front of your counsellor. Serves you right for believing Schmuck and staying mum.

Yes, you just wanted to be that feeling of home for him. Because homes are what people always go back to. Silly you. You were naive to think that you had the kind of love that writers cannot express in stories, nor singers sing in songs.

Writers know better. This type of love would be a waste of ink and paper. And speaking of songs, Taylor Swift has an unending list that might be relevant to you.

But what is love? Infatuation? Or obsession? Maybe just lust? Or Shah Rukh and Kajol being telly appropriate touchy-feely romantics while a hundred background dancers dance in sync with them and their song?

There were happy jumps inside you because of this miscalculated love. You didn't know that hours later it would be a sad jump. A sad jump and tears. Tears and a jump down the hollow infinitely deep. Down and down and down you went.

You do realise that a bit too soon, and a little too fast, you've withered and become a touch-me-not and lashed at people who care to Touch. You. Not. Their foreheads crinkle and crease. They hold your hands and their care spills before the impending question bursts. You look into their concerned eyes and lie. "I'm okay", you say.

You tell everyone that you're a haunting sadcore song that should only get played once in a while. You soothe and pacify in small doses and smother and kill when overdosed. So, you ask them to leave, before you change from medicine to poison and bring them down with you.

Maybe when you die the mortuary cosmetologist will doll you up. She'll hide the slits on your wrists, pat makeup that's two shades lighter on your skin. Your haters will lower you into a coffin and mourn in black uniforms. The people who've stabbed, twisted, pulled your insides, and rendered you voiceless will pity you and whisper that you died so young.

Coming back to Schmuck, when you saw him months later, you angled your head down, wiped your tears, smiled through your Ruby Woo lips, and stopped your legs from shivering underneath your emerald gown. One look at him and you knew that he was unapologetic and oblivious towards the damage he'd done. A clueless someone had replaced you, and she didn't know that he was holding her hand just to go and chirp later about the new lady he'd been sporting on his sleeve.

Just maybe, late into a night, he'll realise the brunt of the damage he's unleashed. He'll learn that memories always leave residues; a half-eaten dinner plate, empty beer cans, and white ash on the tips of his fore and middle fingers. It will all come back. The way he held your hand, the familiar taste of your soup, the long and rambled talks, ringlets of your un-straightened hair tracing patterns on his bed. He'll pull in a mouthful of vapour courtesy his carelessly rolled joint and give up the idea of good trips. He'll be the king of his world when he's sober, but he will succumb. Submit. Cave, to a roll of dry leaves. *Nasha*[1], people say, is what is needed at the end of tiring days. But *Nasha*, you know, is just the temporary return of conscience. He'll mourn for the lover he's burned.

Enough about the *Crown Prince of Flies*.

It's too late to go back to square one. You didn't want drama, you said. You should have stuck to the simpler things in a boyless world; collected pebbles and pressed fall leaves inside books.

It's okay. Take one plate out for dinner, not two. Sit in front of an open book. Plug your earphones in as the walls close in.

James Bay's *Let It Go* and tears.

James Bay's *Let It Go* and tears.

Let It Go. Tears.

1. Nasha: Intoxication

An Old Song Playing in Another Room

I know better than to disturb her when she's reading her tarot cards. It's a precious little ritual to her, flipping those worn-edged secret keepers on their velvet cloth. She's told me a thousand times that she knows the cards themselves have no power, but she likes to use them to align her thoughts. A conduit, or something. A guide.

I take an armchair opposite her, watching as she sits cross-legged on the floor. Her fingernails catch the light, the glossy sheen of paint and smooth topcoat glinting as her long, soft fingers ruminate over the cards. Her eyes are dark and darting back and forth, connecting dots, concentrating. An intense focus has painted shallow lines between her brows, framing her face with small indicators of tension. She'll be thinking over some small possibility, an implication from one faded picture that might pick up in another, some thin thread of the future.

The cards don't interest me. She, however, does.

Her body leans forward, captivated by reading whatever she wants into those faded cards. She reminds me of an old painting in my grandmother's house, some replica on curling yellow paper of a geisha sitting elegantly with her *koto*, her fingers poised above the strings. With her hands outstretched, her fingertips tracing the cards in her lay, it's as if they were strings for her to play. If I close my eyes, I can almost imagine a melody, something mellow and earthy, or haunting perhaps, like a lone cello. I've never heard a *koto* before, so I can let my imagination fill in the blanks. Considering how the fingers pluck at the strings rather than run a bow along them, maybe something more similar to a guitar would be appropriate?

The thought leads me along for a while, filling in the silence between the muffled outside world and the soft *shlick* of cards being turned over, each in their order. I recognise a couple from my vantage point, even with their images upside down. The Tower. The Eleven of Swords. A small smile ghosts on her lips and her eyes meet mine for the merest of moments before she lays down her most recent acquisition. The Lovers. I make a show of my amusement and reach for a book as she reshuffles her deck, beginning her next question. We'll sit here in this companionable silence for a while, maybe, both reading in different ways.

When the sky outside the window is like black silk, glistening with stars and the hum of traffic, maybe then she will sit back. She'll click first one shoulder, then the other, always left side first. Each finger knuckle in turn will be cracked. If one refuses to pop, she may start again from the beginning, or if she can feel in her joint that the capacity is simply not there, she might choose to move on instead. It has become something of a game to me, to watch her little habits, her intricacies.

Once that is complete, she will be open for questions. I'll be able to put my book aside — though I won't fold over the page. She bought me a bookmark one day in a fit of rage, citing the crumpled corners as the root cause. Relationships are like that, I suppose, a slow and steady dance of learning each other, feeling out the other party's likes and dislikes, their goals and their fears. She is my puzzle, and my prize.

If her reading hasn't taken too long, hasn't stretched out like a feline in repose, then I'll ask for some simple answers about her cards. She'll tell me about the importance of flower colours, left hands and right hands, covered shoes or peeping toes. Perhaps, if there is time, she'll fan out her deck like a spectrum of possibilities, show me the card she thinks of as mine.

It's not a positive card, in most readings. I remember being slightly hurt when she told me that — I put no weight to the cards, but nevertheless, being told your loved one associates you with a bad omen is sour to the taste. I've studied the picture before now, looking for whatever connection she sees. A man in a chair, cradling four pentacles. A symbol of possessiveness, deep-seated issues that need to be dealt with and released.

She told me when we first met that she was reminded of a *kintsugi* pot. Something once broken, now repaired with gold. I was holding a door open for her somewhere, she was carrying something heavy. She muttered something that might have been a thank you, but equally might have been something insulting. The day barely lodged in my memory, but it was the beginning of this. Of *us*.

She tells me now, sometimes in those hazy nighttime conversations when neither of us can fall asleep, when the night reaches out into infinity, secure and endless and open to all topics, that she could see scars on me that day. I wear them proudly, nothing physical. I've had hard times. I learned from them. She liked that about me.

It took me much longer to notice her. As much as I thought I avoided social situations, preferred my own company and soft music and old books, she was apart from the crowd even more so. At events — those slim middles of the Venn diagram between my life and hers — she would stand to the side. A wallflower.

I didn't realise until our fourth meeting, at a party where we were once again like two ships in the night, grazing past each other with unintentional apathy, that she was not a wallflower. She, much like me, was an observer, something on the outside by choice, languid eyes following each movement with the casual entertainment of someone with no vested interest. Our eyes met across the heads of drifting individuals, giddy on company and drinks and a pulsing bass. She had smiled. It hadn't been shy — she wasn't ashamed at being caught. No, it had been more like a smirk, a short, slow curve. An acknowledgement. We were the same.

She told me the Four of Pentacles wasn't a bad card, that all cards, even Death, have different meanings. I had already learned the lesson of the card, she told me once, back when we first started living together and I watched her tarot cards with the fascination of novelty. Though, she had said, with a teasing grin and a small shake of one long finger, this did not mean that the card no longer held importance for me. And so, she said, the Four of Pentacles was mine. I was the card of learning to let go and live. Despite that, we both knew, sat on the rug hunched over her cards, that I had no intention of letting her go. I was growth, but not insincerity.

I asked her once, a few months ago, maybe more, what her card was. It was an idle curiosity. She had smiled that same smile, the cat-grin that had first united us across a dimly lit room, and refused to tell me. Let her keep her secrets, she had laughed. She didn't want to give too much away too soon.

Sure, I know if I ever chose to hover intently enough, I could easily discern her significator for myself, but she has asked for privacy, and so I'll respect that. Jokingly, sometimes, she says she'll tell me on certain conditions. Ludicrous quests. Bring me the moon. I want that star. Tell me three things that no one knows, or four things that must never be spoken.

She is full of these superstitions, these things to which I have never given weight. I walk under ladders, and she will let go of my hand to walk around. My first cat was black. She admitted it was cute, but was always wary. Broken mirrors are just a pain to replace, and a possible sharp-edged hazard to be aware of, but to her they're symbols of storms on the horizon, some cosmic karma waiting to bite.

She is like a ripple in the water, glancing in a puddle to see the world inverted, and I enjoy the way she sees things so differently. Some habits have even begun to rub off on me. Like her, I will greet the magpies, each in their turn. If a day goes badly, I might even shrug and say it was a one bird day. Mostly from mimicking her, I never stir my coffee widdershins, and now it feels unnatural to stir the other way around. I can only hope some of my more practical habits have rubbed off on her in return. It would be nice to think we can grow by exchanging these small parts of ourselves.

For now, though, I have no issue with watching her differences. She is a curiosity — no, more than that, an enigma. I have always picked at people, like someone might chew over the Sunday crossword. It's not intended as a demeaning exercise. People simply interest me, just how they interest her. We are watchers. But we are watchers in different senses. They are like stories to her, but like equations to me.

And still, all these thoughts are soundtracked by that soft *schlick* of the cards, a web of fortunes that grows and grows and grows. But, whereas the possibilities that stand before us might have once felt heavy, now they are like a comforting blanket. A future exists between us. It's up to us to see where it leads.

Our lives follow different cycles. Whilst this is part of the end of her day, setting her mind straight before sleep, my day is still ongoing. A midday to her dusk. But I'll let her sleep, sit in the dim light and read or watch her face. Maybe I'll see the dart of dreams, her eyes going to and fro behind her lids as if she were still reading her cards. I'll soak it in — the soft curve of her face, the tight curl of her fingers, that perfect nail polish still in place.

To me, she is these small glimpses. I picture her in a thousand tiny pieces, an intricate weave of the angle of her smile, the way her hair curls when it rains, the smell of her shampoo that lingers in the curve of her ears — all these little things, and more. So many more. I don't care that sometimes we go for days without contact, when the planets and our schedules don't align. It will ache, sure, like a missing tooth my tongue can't ignore, but I know eventually we will have nights like these, with the easy companionship of two people who know this will happen again. And again. And again.

When I wake up, she will be gone. The smell of coffee might linger in the kitchen from her breakfast, maybe the shower will still be fogged with some remnant of moisture or the scent of some floral soap. Her world starts before mine: she must be out and working before I wake. Her absence will hurt, a small and ordinary sting, and I will hold these little pieces close to myself. I build a daily mosaic of her, my personal jigsaw. When I wake, and she is gone, these things will comfort me, like an old song playing in another room.

Do Not Refreeze

Save your breath. We're done.

No—the first thing he heard was the door.

Three grocery bags on the kitchen table. He had just arrived—breathless—from the 24-hour convenience, having walked halfway home before remembering he had promised to pick up the shopping this week. Tomatoes—fridge. The fridge couldn't fully open without crashing into the storage unit opposite. Eggs—cupboard? Cupboard. He pivoted his ass awkwardly to knock the fridge shut and reached upwards. *Four boneless haddock fillets in a protective ice glaze. Keep frozen. Max temp: °C -18.* He tossed them into a bag with the rest of the freezer stuff and headed out of the kitchen.

Their freezer was in the hallway, under the stairs. He felt the coldness pinch at the tip of his nose as the rubber seal popped apart. Squatting slightly, he didn't see the front door open, but heard her keys scratch against the lock. Its hinges gave a brassy shriek as it swung loose.

A more comprehensive floor plan: the usual terraced starter-home setup. Overstuffed kitchen, spilling out into a narrow hallway, rickety stairs twisting upwards into a disproportionately spacious bedroom. A flagship slice of real estate. You could stand in the middle of the bathroom and drum your knuckles on any two walls at once.

He turned to look and she had already thrown her door keys towards him. They skittered across the floor like a small pile of bones and stopped halfway down the hall, nowhere near his feet, but he got the gesture.

•

They meet in a train station. Picture: tall brick arches and pigeons and metal frame benches. Foggy panes in the roof reveal a starless dusk. People dot the platform, smoking, drinking from little paper coffee cups, stabbing at flip phones with chubby fingers, exhaling tiny clouds that float apart in the refrigerated air. There is something enlightening about watching a part of yourself drift between your lips and fade into the world.

Her: leaning against the wall next to an ATM, slim black coat, low-rise jeans and faux fur cuffs, poking absently at a cigarette, pausing occasionally to thumb away the ash, mascara clumping around the *it's-been-a-long-day* type of scowl. Him: eyebrows knotted, shapeless suit, right thumb tapping out a studied apology as scuffed oxfords echo off the tiles, one shirt tail untucked and flapping, the cold air pinching a rosy flush from his cheeks.

They meet by an ATM in a train station. He fumbles his wallet, still typing, hits send, grimaces at his account balance. He pauses for a few seconds while a tannoy announcement floods the platform with fuzzy static, splashing distortedly off the brickwork, and then withdraws a few notes. He glances cautiously towards her, then asks to bum a cigarette. She takes a long drag then lowers her hand, eyes scanning his ragged crew cut, the loose shirt tail, his battered eye-bags, mouth smudged with the last traces of a hurried takeout—sizing him up, as it goes—then raises her chin and blows a pronounced plume of smoke just past his face. A few seconds pass as the smoke settles into the shoulder of his blazer. Teases at his lips and his nostrils.

She shrugs. Why not.

She drops her cigarette and squashes away the embers with a purposeful toe, before knocking two more straights from the box. A lengthy supply train stampedes through the station with a guttural clatter. The air shakes so violently that it threatens to lift the skin from their skeletons.

•

He felt the cosy air hustle out of the hallway. She didn't walk in, but lingered, ever-so-faintly swaying, in her slim black coat with its faux fur cuffs that she had worn by the ATM in the train station, eyes angled vaguely toward his forehead.

Save your breath. We're done.

It wasn't aggressive. It wasn't directed at him so much as it was simply announced in his direction. For a moment, they stood there in silence, metres apart in the hallway, while the wind curled quietly through the open door and nudged at her hair.

He fell back on his tried and tested method. He tried to find the anger in her eyes; to hear the thunder drumming through her voice; to spot her tear ducts as they inflated like tiny balloons behind her cheeks. He waited for the waver of desperation in her voice, but she just stood there, silent. Footnote: the movies don't prepare you for the silences. The way words hang like undeveloped film in a darkroom, soggy and separate in the air. The gut reaction is to annotate, to pick out the punctuation and the pauses that were never really there when the words float out into space and hang in your ears and your head for a second or a week or the rest of your life.

Remove from foil, taking care as excess steam could burn.

•

He walks into the small, packed, stuffy office that has been his workplace for almost four years—a period in which he has secured about half a square metre of desk, a chunky CRT desktop, a telephone and a drawer that jars as it opens, so he barely uses it—at around eleven. He manages to cough up a laugh or two with his co-workers in the kitchen, and then, a little drowsy, returns to his telephone and hopes he can stumble upon some unsuspecting work-from-home-parent to buffer that commission. A new colleague has recently started to distribute strawberry dragées from the vending machine during this time, to lift the mood. She has short ginger hair and freckles on her nose.

He pauses over his work space, assessing the clutter between the narrow corners. The usual ensemble: staplers, post-it notes, several used mugs and a picture taken two years after they had shared that cigarette in the station. They had stood in front of the new house and posed, grinning in the open doorway, backed by a narrow hallway and rickety stairs. They had built a life out of a starless moment and packed the rest with bus routes and nicotine patches and door keys and compact bathroom walls and boneless haddock fillets.

Five-thirty: he splits open his packet sandwiches and quickly demolishes the first before returning to the phone; dinner time was *the* peak stretch to catch the suburban punters by their landlines. Move the goalposts. By seven, sales start to stall. He picks at the stale edges of the remaining sandwich and heads to the kitchen to make small-talk and suckle down a strawberry dragée. He struggles to remember relocating the picture from his desk to the drawer—the drawer that jars as it opens, so he barely uses it—but two thick, dustless contours frown up at him in its absence. Move the goalposts.

Ten, maybe eleven: he meanders listlessly in the direction of a cheap pizza joint, so exhausted that he doesn't feel hungry and so hungry he doesn't feel exhausted. They had built a life out of a starless moment and the world had plugged the gaps.

A familiar voice sounds from the queue behind him, and he turns to see short ginger hair. The freckles on her nose dilate as she smiles back.

•

Save your breath. We're done.

The movies don't prepare you for the silences. They script out what you say and how you say it and fill in the blanks with a ballad or a love song or something upbeat from the 80s because it's ironic. *We have given you these cooking instructions as a guide only.* A coldness pinched at the tip of his nose and the front door shrieked open and the keys skittered across the floor like a small pile of bones and stopped halfway down the hall, nowhere near his feet.

•

The showing doesn't start till eight thirty.

He reminds her.

He reminds her of this while she perches on the windowsill in their bath room, applying makeup.

She scratches at the inside of her palm with her thumbnail. We need to be at the restaurant by six.

He doesn't reply.

She pauses to wipe the tinge of breath from her mirror. In case they're busy.

She continues to hurriedly dab at her face while he brushes his teeth and she swears at him when their elbows collide. A throat-vowel apology emerges through the foam. He finishes, spits a few times, and transfers his cell phone from his left pocket to his right, so that she can't take it out for an absent-minded skim during the boring parts of the film.

He had narrowly avoided allowing the word *affair* to snake across his mind and attach itself to the situation; it was too broad a term, its breathy syllables too easily blowing over the specifics. It had started with tugs at his shirt collar, with glances to his neck and lips in public washrooms, and often in car windows as he passed. It had developed into buried photographs. Strawberry dragées. Hushed phone calls. Dimmed brightness. Lipstick on both wine glasses, keep the receipt. It had emerged as a habit that swelled slowly and conquered his mind, pitching electric fences around every section of his daily routine.

This was not a conscious strategy. Two lists of "good" and "bad" restaurants had taken form in his mind to avoid cross-contamination. More white space than usual had blossomed across the calendar pinned to the fridge—the fridge that couldn't fully open without crashing into the storage unit opposite—and timetabling had migrated from his home computer to his chunky CRT work desktop. Excuses armed themselves, ready in their silos, weeks before it was necessary to launch them. Mass deleting correspondence had become second nature. It was not a conscious strategy. It was like putting on deodorant, or clothes.

He leans forward, perched inelegantly on the rickety stairs, and battles with his laces. He looks up, spotting the sunlight as it drifts through the open door and saturates her face, then frowns, catching himself checking her nose for freckles.

•

He opened his mouth to speak, to offer something to fill the space between them, an explanation, an apology, a justification, a compliment, a plea, a joke, *something*, but before he could prize the words from their sticky chambers she evaporated into the doorway, hair stirring in a subtle arc, and pulled the door noiselessly shut behind her. *Once defrosted use within 24 hours, do not refreeze.*

In the following months, he stripped her words bare, tried to find some furtive clue between each syllable, traced them in the condensation of the shower curtain, but, ultimately, they always spelled out the same thing. Save your breath. We're done.

The keyhole quivered softly like a half-formed question mark as she pulled the door noiselessly shut behind her and he stood in the hallway, still, waiting for someone to speak.

•

They lean against the wall by an ATM, taking syncopated kisses of tobacco and nicotine, and watch people drip from the platform onto the metal carriages that slide in and out of vision. The passengers flop limply into faded seats and disfigure as a tarry cloud drifts up from between her lips and shuffles up the image.

She watches the cloud dissipate, then gestures with her cigarette. That's your train.

I know.

They blow thick jets of smoke as his train creaks and pulls away, watching the parts of themselves rise and fade into the air.

•

Save your breath. We're done.

The keyhole quivered softly, then fell silent, and he realised that he'd mistaken the quietness of the exit for the curve of a question mark and that she had never asked a question and neither had he and the answer had already skittered across the floor like a small pile of bones and stopped halfway down the hall, nowhere near his feet.

The Sound of her Essence

She is talking, talking, talking. Words. *"The word senex in Dante's Paradise..."* She's so tiny, so skinny. Her bones. Does She ever eat?
I saw Her eating a chocolate bar the other day, while standing in front of the machines... I have an apple and I should eat an apple.

I should pay attention. If She asks me questions I won't know what to say. And then She'd tell my parents I don't listen in her lessons.

Dante. *"Beatrice and her eyes"*... Her eyes are just brown, just fine. Mine are prettier. Am *I* prettier? *"... metaphor"* the Inferno was better. And She was better at explaining it. She was a better teacher, back then. I liked Her, do I like Her now?

I can see Her black bra through the white t-shirt.

She is so skinny. How can She stand in front of the whole class and not fall?

Like a flat figure... a paper doll with ruined edges.

Kind of worried for Her. Envious? No, maybe, a bit.

Anna, the other day: *"I've seen Her in front of my house, arguing with a man"*. Anna is so lucky to be Her neighbour.

But he was: beard and good-looking. Was it day? It was night. Yes, night. Why does She have a good-looking guy? She is skinny, that's the reason.

But, they were fighting. It was her fault. It was his fault. Was it? I have to fit.

"Dante's syntax..." I'm not following. Follllowwwwing. Lllll, wwww. Wwwwave, llllake.

He kissed me at Bracciano Lake. When he kissed me... I said "oh", but I wasn't surprised, and I liked it, but not really. And he said, he looked at me, and said "Pretty". But also, he looked at me and also, what did he say? "Fat"? "You got fat"? No. I, "oh" and he, "Pretty, I like your curves."

Do I have curves? Does it mean I am fat? But I said "oh" and I liked it, but not really.

Did he kiss Her, instead? Anna didn't say so. Nah, God knows why they were fighting.

When he kissed me – my He, of course, not Hers – he tasted like coffee.

And "no" but it meant "yes" and "oh", as if I was surprised. But I wasn't. And, is She tiny but She still has a boyfriend? But, was *he* Her boyfriend?

"Beatrice." Good name, for a child. Do I want a child? Do they have a child? They do not, and I know this. But if they did… She can't have one, too little, so little it seems I can see through Her. Her bones seem to pass Her skin. Do they break it? Is *She* broken? Maybe, inside, where I can't see. Broken and destroyed. A child could break Her, piercing her skin; I could break Her, like a porcelain doll. I can break Her, Her frail body. I could break it by pushing just a little.

Only squeezing Her in my hand. She is so skinny, too skinny.

Too little. Too frail. I want to hear the sound. And Her sound.

The sound of Her bones, breaking.

Is that the sound of Her essence?

Hustle Tomorrow, Not Today

Tomorrow was going to be a great day. My nails were recently polished and my hair was braided. My stylist, who lived down the road of our estate where I lived with my dad, my brothers and my little sister, had opened her shop on my request. She had applied the coconut-scented hair spray on my braids. The smell filled the entire salon and I handed over the sum of five thousand naira[1], the largest amount of money I have ever paid a stylist. I could see the smile creep by the sides of her mouth as she counted the notes.

Well, I wouldn't be spending naira for the next one year. It was better to be prepared for the life that I would live in the United Kingdom. When I received the email from the government agency, I cracked into a smile and an excited jump that startled my dad. He shouted from the sitting room and asked if I drank sugar. It was the moment I had been waiting for, ever since I applied for that job. The constant fear, the persistent prayers and the impatience I felt every time my dad would ask me if I had gotten feedback from the agency was finally allayed. It was also the day I would see my boyfriend for the last time. We had planned to visit the Genesis Cinemas centre at Maryland to see a movie. Hustlers. I was going to watch the movie only out of curiosity. I wanted to know how they struggled and survived the lifestyle they chose. Perhaps, a green light would suddenly pop out and more ideas on strategising and hustling would come to light. All these were meant to happen tomorrow. But firstly, I had to get my vaccination shot at the Port Health Centre, 10 miles from the airport. The airport I would be visiting after spending twenty-five years in the confines of my country.

I arrived at the Port Health Centre at about 12 noon. As I moved closer to the entrance, I saw a 6-foot middle-aged man, his bleached skin the colour of Khaled Hosseini's *A Thousand Splendid Suns* book cover. I knew because it was my current read. He was by the entrance, clad in a native *Yoruba* shirt and trousers made of the colour of cream and his hands were in his pockets. The entrance was made of iron, rusted due to its old age, and glass stained by the harshness of the weather. I took in a deep breath and moved closer, hoping he would move out of the way. He noticed me and removed his hands from his pocket. I greeted him with a slight nod of my head and stepped into the clearing which served as the reception area, but it had no receptionist or doorman to welcome us. It had long brown benches with backrests. Seated on them were a dark-skinned man and his son, some thin-looking girls and another woman who wore *Dunlop* slippers. Each of them wore a glum, exhausted expression. They must have been waiting for a while, but that wasn't surprising. It was something we had become accustomed to.

I walked slowly and sat beside the dark-skinned man who was speaking to his son in an assured tone, almost inaudible. I fiddled with my phone, scrolling through my feed for something engaging but all that kept popping up was news about the impending Big Brother Naija Final Show. I hissed and logged out of the social network, turning off my data and clearing my browsing history. It was getting clogged anyway and it was bound to become more clogged by the end of the week.

I looked up from my phone, a bit confused about what I should do but I understood that everyone who sat in the faux reception area came for the same thing to be administered the yellow fever vaccine. It was not mandatory for me as I was going to the United Kingdom, but one could not be sure of things these days. You had to be crazy to be unprepared for the worst in this country. I sat patiently, hoping that soon, an official would be kind enough to ask me what I wanted and I'd be on my jolly way. I looked at the time again. It was 12:34 pm. I had time but I was not happy about spending up to two hours sitting at the reception.

The Port Health Service Centre was open from 8 am to 4 pm all through Monday to Friday so I didn't think I was too late to get a shot. More people were still coming into the reception area and each had with them their payment receipts, printed off onsite or online, just like I did.

So, I sat there, on the hard wooden bench in this reception area, shifting my foot noisily on the hard floor. I kept watching as other people came in, walked right through the vaccination doors, had their shots and walked right out with smiles. I was tempted to slap it off but alas, I did not have the nerve or the *liver*[2] to do so.

Seconds turned into minutes and minutes into three hours; I was sitting and pacing around the reception area in frustration trying to get the attention of an official. I was fidgeting silently when one of them saw me. He donned an exasperated smile and placed his hand on the door handle of the vaccination room. He turned his face toward the stacks of payment receipts he had collected from other people and turned back to me.

'Come back tomorrow,' he said to me. He gave me a helpless look and walked off to meet the other folk. They started to chat incessantly. I tried to speak up, but my voice only sounded like the whistle of an air conditioning machine.

'I have been here for three hours. I have been sitting all along.' I tried to sound as desperate as possible, but I was lying. I was mad and angry. I wanted to shout in that reception area like a boss and tell them off and complain about their inept customer service operations. My bladder started to signal to me. Oh well, I had to get to the bathroom as soon as I had that shot and got out of there. So, I went back to my seat and let out a small prayer under my breath. *Wee-wee, please go back now*. Wrong time for the forces of nature to begin expressing their power over my physicality.

Whilst I prayed my predicament away, the doctor who had a low haircut and a pair of black spectacles came out with a file in hand and everyone gathered around her with questions, 'When is your flight?' the doctor asked us one after another. The others were men. 'Tomorrow', 'today.' No one dared to mention a later time because of the urgency of the shot we wanted to take. But foolish me. Miss Smartypants! The nurse, I later figured out she was a nurse, not a doctor.

'When is your flight?' she asked, looking over her spectacles. I had a smile on like a kid who was denied chocolate and was about to burst into a song of tears. 'Umm...in about two weeks?', I replied unsure with my hand reaching for the back of my head. I was trying to be cute.

She shook her head.

I read it.

'Tomorrow.'

Tomorrow! For the second time? I have been waiting for a long time to have this shot taken. How could she tell me to come back tomorrow? Who does that? Why so heartless? I thought of the movie I was going to miss. I thought of my boyfriend I was meant to see. I wouldn't get the chance if I did not get my vaccination done today. Tomorrow was booked. My heart became a field with football players kicking the grass. I did not have the courage to call the nurse out. One of the guys came close to me and whispered in my ears. 'You should have told her your flight is today.' I was trying hard to come up with an excuse for not having thought of the lie sooner, but I suppose it wasn't in my nature. But lying is a human trait, is it not? And one by one, the guys all went into the vaccination room to have their shots taken while I paced with hope in that reception area. In a few minutes the reception area was cleared, and we had three others left. I was supposedly the last person to take a shot. Shot, not to be dead but live. I opened the door to the vaccination office with the nurse about to pack up the syringes.

'Sisi?[3]' She called me. 'You are still here?'

Interesting! I thought she asked me to come back tomorrow.

'Sit down.'

I sat on the plastic chair in the office.

'Open wide,' she said. I opened my mouth and she squeezed two to three drops of the polio vaccine in my mouth. I couldn't remember what it tasted like, but it was bitter and alien, and I knew something had been put into my system. How my body was to react I wasn't sure at all. She wiped her hands with a sanitary napkin and poured methylated spirit into cotton wool. She beckoned on me to hold out my arm whilc she cleaned the spot she'd inject, taking quick but gentle swipes. Tossing the used wool into the bin underneath the wooden table close to me, I took a quick tour of the room. It was a typical four-corner room with ash-washed walls and had a window without curtains. If it had curtains, I was certain they'd be stolen. She brought out the yellow fever syringe. I grimaced. I am a big girl who is not afraid of the needle, but I like to feign a little fear — I don't know who the

fear is for. Perhaps, an unknown friend who was in the air watching me and the nurse as she played nurse. The needle hardly stung but the vaccine, boy, I could feel it coursing through my veins into my bloodstream.
I wanted to scream 'Ouch!', but my pride restrained me, and I walked out of the vaccination room. Smiling. Happy that I didn't lie and still had my pride intact and my truth. But perhaps, if I had lied, I would have been out of this ugly reception area sooner and would not have wasted as much time as I did pacing the floor with the others who had gone before me.

I stepped out of the reception into the garden in front of the centre, ordering an Uber. I saw the same middle-aged man again. He was chatting up a young girl my age. As I walked past them, I heard him say to her, 'Come back tomorrow.'

I breathed out a sigh of relief, my feet activating into a dance and my hair grazing the back of my neck. My tomorrow was fixed, Hustlers, Cardi B and J-Lo.

1. Naira – Nigerian currency
2. Liver – Nigerian Pidgin Slang for 'courage'
3. Sisi – Nigerian Pidgin Slang for 'young lady'

Brake Lights

Civilisation, that glossy golden sheen, like dripping honey that glues your fingers to your lips. It rots your teeth. Those sleepwalking city lights aimlessly blinding through the rain, hazed and burning like neon wildfire. Badges and tie-pins dazzle in glass windows, with those diamond-eyed sharks dressed in glitter, looping in muted waves. The salty geometry becomes tangled in my eyes, until everything felt very real—very familiar. Just watch those mannequin bodies pulsing to the smoke detector throb of Monday night. That splendour of seizing limbs sticky with lip-gloss and nicotine patches, all woven together into life jackets pumped and tearing at the edges of a welted-on fast-food pin near to burst. Pockets chattered, weighed down by copper pennies, gory with cola stains. They float through crowds, boxed up in suspended plastic, spinning round and round to the echo of a ceiling fan.

Here, it rains in summer. Condensation dewy and scalding, even at night, seeping out of the long glass bodies itching to reach the sky. These mountains made of hissing bent steel, rusting the briefcases that churn in and out belonging to consciousness-possessed suits. The squeaky endless inertia that lathers under groping hands, searching their trousers for their keys in the dark cognitive fog. The television glows, fire green in an oil spill of fetishes and commodities splayed out in prismatic shadows of printed circuits. An exhaust pipe cracks and breaks within the pumping house of electricity and they close their eyes and remember that this is not their home, just before the nausea sinks in again.

Blaring engines ripple through the tarmac with brake lights dribbling cherry red into the jewelled street. Bodies stab into leather seats, clenching and tearing them, digging into the soft underbelly and plunging sharp hooked nails into gasoline skin. The rubber snaps and stretches beneath the weight, hands fingering seat belts with angles and fondling thumbs. Wheels burst into black ribbons that dress the roads, indistinguishable from the next. Into the car, into the shell. Those creeping bluebottle cases, curling cages of virtual vertebrae. They clutter down the highway, flashing amber cuticles, funnelling liquid spoils.

But you creep away, etch out of the electric throb of perfunctory whispers into the oaky wash. The windows turn heaving silver as the ignition lilts across the success of night. Outside, bluebells bend to east winds, and crowns of birches twirl in pleasant gushes of grey skin. The maddening chatter hushes and flashes against the jackdaw's gentle feather, damp with dew, as snowdrops hang in broken-necked opulence, dripping into running streams like loose bones in dreams.

The woods outside are softer. They're dark and the din has stopped. Wet stars giggle breathlessly as you lie back against the moss. You remember that these mountains were meant to stay out of reach.

An Accident at the Underground Railway Station

It was 3.45 p.m. when Thomas walked into the underground railway station, exactly two hours earlier than he did every day. He lifted his eyes, without any certain target to look at, and was attracted, once again, by the large sign on the wall that read: 'THE PROCESS MUST BE QUICK AND SMOOTH'. It was a sign of rather impressive size. The black letters looked unusually striking against a bright yellow background, as though every stroke could pop out the next second.

Thomas wondered what that sign actually meant. His attention was always drawn to it when he took the underground at dusk, but today the question seemed especially urgent. What did 'THE PROCESS MUST BE QUICK AND SMOOTH' mean? It was probably a notice telling the passengers to get on and off trains quickly. But it could also be an advertisement of some so-called 'amazing product' that would help one cope with daily chores. It was hard to say, Thomas thought, when the train arrived at 3.50 p.m.

Thomas stepped aside cautiously, in case he might block the way of any running passengers or their unwieldy belongings. There were fewer people at the station than he usually saw, but he still had to find an empty corner to stand in to give room to queuing people. He, on the other hand, was not going to board the train. In fact, this should not have been the time for him to appear in the underground railway station.

Earlier this afternoon, when he was waiting for the lift in the office building, he knew something had gone utterly wrong in his life – not as scheduled, out of track ... 'The train is arriving' ... and he must grasp his last opportunity to fix it. He checked his notebook again when the lift stopped at the 6th floor: the meeting was scheduled at 2.00 p.m., with Ms. Williams, at Room 602. He adjusted the collar of his shirt when walking quickly towards the end of the corridor, passing the 'No Smoking', 'No Speaking', and the curious 'No Standing Here' signs... 'Mind the gap when you are boarding'... Other details now seemed rather confused. However, he could remember clearly how he rehearsed his speech behind the closed door of Room 602, the rhythm of blood throbbing in his neck while he spoke, and the intermittent signal sounds given by some machine at one corner of the room.

Ms. Williams looked attentive and said nothing until Thomas had finished. Her countenance remained placid throughout the time, except that there was a slight curve gradually formed by her thin lips, which he interpreted as a smile.

'If I have understood you correctly, Mr. Johnson,' Ms. Williams replied, after a pause, 'you are here to talk about the decision, right?'

He remembered he had made some gesture of assent.

'Thank you very much for coming and talking about how you feel, Mr. Johnson. But I'm afraid you have made a mistake. The board haven't read the documents you've been explaining, but whatever the case, this decision is definitely not due to any problem in your documents. Actually, you don't need to worry about your documents. They're fine.'

He blinked and breathed deeply to look less nervous. Now that he knew his documents were flawless, it was more convincing that the decision must have been made from some grudge against him – or someone's misrepresentation of his abilities – that was inevitable in his situation. He was ready to make a desperate defence of himself, whether others would listen or not, when Ms. Williams added, 'My advice is that you should not take it too seriously. The decision, I hope you would understand, was made in accordance with a change to our department's policy this year. You were all considered on an equal footing – it's really not your fault, Mr. Johnson.'

Now *that* was a discovery. 'It's not your fault', what did that mean? It might indeed be a proof of his innocence – but it could also mean that he did not need any fault to be victimised – or maybe it implied that the decision was nobody's fault at all, and everything simply happened by chance –

'Excuse me!' a passenger said to Thomas, almost bumping into him while running to catch the 3.55 p.m. train. The man's mobile phone dropped on the ground as he rushed by Thomas's side. Some part of it was broken, and the passenger, in a hurry to board the train, quickly picked it up and put it back into his pocket, without even glancing back. His face immediately disappeared among so many faces looking through the opening doors.

Thomas thought he knew the face of that passenger. Perhaps he saw it every day when he took the underground. But he probably just mistook that face for someone else's. He watched the moving crowd, half admiringly, half fearfully. He wondered whether some accident had occurred in this busy station. After all, the 'mind the gap' announcement must have been recorded for a reason – should some unfortunate guy forget to stand behind the line on the platform and get smashed by the whizzing train – it could be *anyone*. A machine would not pick its victim.

At this idea, Thomas suddenly felt his mind began to reflect randomly, at a very quick speed and uncontrolled. He remembered how he had been trying to bear all problems in life with firmness, and to reconcile high aspirations with reality. He was strong enough to bury in his heart the bitterness of his experience in the department, and face enmity with patience. He had envisioned the moment when he could prove himself and forget all bitterness with a triumphant smile.

Yet *now* he saw the mistake he had made. He had thought he was the chosen one, out of bias, or envy, to suffer from consequences of that significant decision. He had almost felt certain that the abrupt termination of his career in the department was related to his idiosyncrasy and personal conducts, which he would not regret even if someone disliked them. He had even fancied he was like a martyr, who made sacrifice for his principles – But what if he had been wrong from the very beginning? Surely Ms. Williams might not have told him everything, yet what she said was very possibly the fact. He had taken everything 'too seriously'. After all, he never had the slightest proof of the hatred he had once been so sure that others had against him. The truth was, Thomas now realised with pain, not many people in the department could remember his name, and he seldom talked. He could not convince himself that someone in the department had designed the decision as a plot just because they had to get rid of him. The greater chance was that the decision was made out of necessity, not maliciousness, and his name happened to be the result of a kind of lottery.

Thomas looked at the crowd with horror. There were so many, so many people who were not him but similar, coming and going at random, to unknown destinations. He had stopped romanticising life long ago, and had given up believing that each event in life would follow a clear logic and reach a meaningful conclusion. No, he did not ask for that much.
He understood that life was never predictable, and though he did not have the best of luck, he had learnt to be contented with what he had got. It was this general satisfaction with the status quo that made him prudent, punctilious, and punctual. He felt contented when he worked alone late at night for a goal he did not understand. He felt contented when remaining silent during those moments he deemed it inappropriate for him to speak. He felt contented when he caught the underground train at 8.00 a.m. in the morning and at 5.45 p.m. in the evening. And what is more, he did not let these routines make him indifferent. In a secret place deep in his heart he had hope – a strong hope – that someday he would finally find true happiness in life, and that this knowledge was deferred would only make it the more desirable… 'The train will arrive in 2 minutes' … as long as he kept waiting and being prudent.

Yet now this waiting was impossible. No doubt the decision had changed forever the lifestyle he had got used to. What upset him most, however, was the thought that his life was ruined, at least for the coming years, yet no one had written his tragedy. He was not a tragic hero, for no one had expected that he happened to be the outcome of the decision. Nor was there a villain in his story, for nobody targeted him. His catastrophe was a complete accident, his epiphany nonexistent, and his personal flaw inconsequential.

Suddenly people began to murmur in the crowd – it was already 4.00 p.m., but the train was delayed. Some people walked a little closer to the platform edge and looked impatiently towards the direction from which the train should come, and Thomas followed them mechanically, till he became the first person in a queue. The station seemed unusually stuffy, and Thomas felt he would get drowned in waves of noises and movements.

Emerging from the waves were some young women, whose facial expressions became portraits of anxiety and disgust. Over there, a bad-tempered old man started to shout swear words, and a toddler happened to burst out crying bitterly. Thomas thought it was indeed time to leave this station – but where should he go today after getting on a train? The crowd of people became increasingly anxious. Every second seemed unbearable.

He looked around unconsciously, as if to find an exit. Just then, he caught sight of that 'THE PROCESS MUST BE QUICK AND SMOOTH' sign again. It was right there, behind his back. The black letters appeared intimidatingly large and striking. Thomas gazed at the sign like one addicted to it, for there seemed to be an inner power screaming at him and distorting every stroke on the board.

'There it comes.' uttered someone as the train arrived — at last — when the entire station was at the brink of chaos. Perhaps due to the delay, the underground train never seemed to have run at a greater speed or with a louder whizz than at this moment. At exactly this moment Thomas saw, finally, the actual meaning of 'THE PROCESS MUST BE QUICK AND SMOOTH' – it was a revelation, a decree, a cure, and a curse for him. He moved along with flocking people. His mind was determined, and his footsteps were steady. THE PROCESS MUST BE QUICK AND SMOOTH.

The next morning, it was reported in the news that an accident happened in an underground railway station. A young man of medium height was said to have fallen from the platform and been killed by an approaching train. The public felt relieved once the police had confirmed that it was a suicide case. No psychopath had pushed the young man off, nor was there any problem with the width of the gap between the platform and the track. The accident happened at 4.08 p.m. Due to the time required to clean up the track, transportation during the rush hours was unfortunately affected.

AUTHOR BIOS

in alphabetical order

Josh Allsop

josh.allsop95@outlook.com

Josh Allsop is a first-year PhD candidate in Creative Writing at Durham University, where he is researching ontological difficulty and labour in the poetry of J.H. Prynne and Geoffrey Hill. His poems have been published in Blackbox Manifold, Pif Magazine, and the Poetry Birmingham Literary Journal.

Janina Arndt

janina.arndt.writer@gmail.com

Janina Arndt is currently studying an MA in Creative Writing at Durham University, after being awarded a first-class degree in English Studies from Heidelberg University. Besides writing, she enjoys storytelling in every medium, which inspires her experiments with form. She has won three youth awards from Girls Go Movie and Club Arte for her short films, and staged several of her own plays with Durham Student Theatre and Aidan's Creative Writing Society.

Lucy Atkinson

atkinsonlucy@outlook.com

Lucy Atkinson is a North-East born poet and playwright currently studying a MA in creative writing at Durham University. She is a graduate in English and creative writing from Manchester Metropolitan University where she earned a first class degree. As of the beginning of 2020 she has published poetry in a number of reputable poetry magazines such as Acumen and Agenda. Her first play *'As It Was'* was awarded the Russell Whiteley prize for new writing at Sedgefield drama festival and published by Lazy Bee Scripts in December 2019.

Theo Breet

breet.theo@gmail.com

Theo Breet is a fiction writer and graduate from Bristol, currently pursuing an MA in Creative Writing at Durham University. With a background in history, he is particularly interested in speculative fiction, the philosophy of religion and the natural world.

Rory Clarkson

rorybclarkson@hotmail.co.uk.

Rory Clarkson is a first year PhD student at Durham University. He's been writing for many years and has amassed a large collection of unpublished work. His research interests focus around contemporary poetry, with his thesis on transnationality of the modern elegy. Aged 24, this is his first publication.

Rosie Crocker

rosie.crocker98@sky.com

Rosie Crocker is a current student of Twentieth and Twenty-First Century Literature at Durham University. She is a graduate of Cardiff University, and writes short vignettes about both cities when not out losing pub quizzes or befriending cats.

Laura Day

laura.day1995@hotmail.co.uk

Laura Day is a PhD student, focussing on the poetry and prose of Cumbrian writer Norman Nicholson. She also works part-time in the Office of the Pro-Vice-Chancellor for Colleges at the University, and is one of the first students of the South College. Born and bred on a hill sheep farm in Cumbria, Laura came to Durham to study for her MA in 2017, following her BA studies at St John's College, Cambridge. When not studying or working, Laura is a keen cyclist and hill-walker, and can often be found planning her next adventure in the Scottish Highlands.

Cassidy Harvard-Davies

cassidy.harvard@gmail.com

Cassidy Harvard-Davies is an MA Creative Writing student at Durham University. She graduated from the University of Southampton with a BA in English in 2019 and writes both poetry and prose fiction. Her research interests include mental health, mythology, and gender within literature, and she hopes to pursue a PhD in the near future. She is currently writing a novel told in haiku, because she enjoys a challenge.

Finn Haunch

fhaunch@gmail.com

Finn Haunch was raised just outside of Leeds, although he was born in Durham. He completed his undergraduate degree last year and is currently studying for an MA, specialising in Modernist literature. He enjoys cutting wood in his spare time.

Ethan Hemmati

ethan.hemmati@gmail.com

Ethan Hemmati is a fiction writer and literature student from Edinburgh. He holds a BA from University of Sheffield and is currently studying for an MA at Durham University. He occasionally writes for theatre.

Avleen Kaur

akl.avleen@gmail.com

Avleen is a postbox who learns to write poetry so she can deliver better letters to the world. She is currently pursuing a Masters in Creative Writing at Durham University. Her work reflects her interest in the universality of emotions, uniqueness of relationships and the absurdity of life. She is also intrigued by issues of colonialism, the partition of the Indian sub-continent and our associations with language and translation. She has recently launched an interactive magazine called 'Breather' that brings human interest stories to young adults. During her MA in English (Panjab University, India), she participated in literary fests, panel discussions, gave writing workshops and became a TEDx speaker.

Annabel Mahoney

Website: annabelmahoney.com

Annabel Mahoney's writing has been shortlisted for awards by the Human Rights Watch, The Literary Association and Forward Poetry and published widely in national and international literary journals. She is the author of two books, *Wyf-King* (Lapwing Publications, 2019) and *St Crispin in the Trenches* (Another New Calligraphy, 2020). Her third collection, *All of this ground and influence*, is currently under consideration for the Eric Gregory Award.

Matthew McKenzie

matthew.t.levitt@gmail.com

Matthew McKenzie is a fiction writer from West London, currently pursuing an MA in Creative Writing at Durham University following his BSc in Biological Sciences. He is interested in people, speculative fiction which pushes the boundaries of modern science and reality, and in connecting to his Afro-Caribbean heritage through writing. Often found doing more research than writing, he likes to portray fictional characters with complex intersectional identities and exploring themes of sexuality, race, mental health and the environment.

Kleopatra Olympiou

kleopatrao@hotmail.com

Kleopatra Olympiou is a writer from Cyprus, currently pursuing a Creative Writing MA at Durham University. She writes for Durham's student newspaper, Palatinate, where she also works as Features Editor.

Victoria Penn

vickyjpenn@hotmail.com

Victoria Penn is a current PhD student focusing on water and identity in the poetry of Jorie Graham and Alice Oswald. She loves the way water trickles through the world, how it rests in some places and flows in others, and how it echoes poetry in all of its comings and goings.

Upasana Pradhan

upasanapradhan1994@gmail.com

Upasana Pradhan was born and raised in India. Currently studying an MA in Creative Writing at Durham University. She phases out of conversations all the time and if you put her on a stage she'll bite you. Being a magnet for anything unusual, she writes stories with eccentric characters. Her favourite word is turquoise. Also, when she's shitty rich, she'll ask Angus and Julia Stone to play Chateau at her wedding.

Imogen Sharpe

imogenlois.sharpe@gmail.com

Imogen Sharpe is a postgraduate Masters student in English Literary Studies, with a special interest in Old Norse. She also studied her Bachelors in English Literature at Durham University, where she first developed an interest in creative writing. During this time, she received the J. R Watson prize, was Vice-Captain for DUQC's Durhamstrang, and volunteered with New Writing North as part of the Durham Book Festival. Currently, she is working towards her Old Norse-related dissertation, whilst serving as a course representative for English MA students.

James Shiers

jamesshiersuk@gmail.com

James Shiers has been described as abrupt.

Claudia Sterbini

C.Sterbini1@uni.brighton.ac.uk

Claudia Sterbini is an MA student in English Studies at Durham University and achieved a BA in English Literature at the University of Sussex. Born in Italy, she has worked variously as a freelance journalist and editor for both Italian and British journals, publishing articles concerned with literature, philosophy and politics. She has worked with poetry and scriptwriting, but most often returns to her passion for short stories, which have been published in Italian magazines. Her narratives usually feature psychological studies or plots tending towards magical realism.

Rachael Wanogho

wanoghorachael@gmail.com, website: rachaelwanogho.com

Rachael Wanogho is a writer, born and raised in Nigeria. Before undertaking her MA in Creative Writing at Durham University, she graduated with a BA in Mass Communication and has interests in digital media content. She writes for the Durham Probono Blog which centres on diverse issues in society. Her writing is highly influenced by her interest in people, romance and societal change. When she's not writing, she's creating video content on her Youtube channel. This is her first publication.

Tula Wild

tula.s.wild@gmail.com

Tula Wild is currently pursuing a Twentieth and Twenty-First Century Literary Studies MA at Durham University. She is a passionate reader, writer, and sketcher. When she's not campaigning for Mental Health charities and the environment, you can usually find her in your local garden centre buying another plant that she probably shouldn't be buying.

WU, You (Helen)

helen_wu_you@163.com

WU, You was born in Shanghai, China. She studied English literature at the Chinese University of Hong Kong, before taking the Creative Writing MA programme at Durham University. She composes prose fiction, poetry, as well as drama. Her writing style is influenced by her interest in Shakespeare and Romanticism, and opera and cinema are also her secret sources of inspiration. Apart from writing, she also views literary translation between English and Chinese as her lifelong passion.

Chutian Xiao

xiaochutian@126.com

Chutian Xiao is a PhD student from China, studying English at Durham University. His thesis title is 'A Buddhist Reading of T. S. Eliot's Poetry'. He is also the author of *Blue Bird* ('青鸟'), a collection of poems which was published in China by Hangzhou Press.